ADULT READING SERIES
Challenger 1

COREA
MURPHY

NEW READERS PRESS
Publishing Division of Laubach Literacy International
Syracuse, New York

ISBN 0-88336-781-5

EACH ONE TEACH ONE

© 1985
New Readers Press
Publishing Division of Laubach Literacy International
Box 131, Syracuse, New York 13210

Printed in the United States of America

Designed by Chris Steenwerth
Cover by Chris Steenwerth

Cover photo by Comstock

9

About the Author

Corea Murphy has worked in the field of education since the early 1960s. In addition to classroom and tutorial teaching, Ms. Murphy has developed language arts curriculum guides for public high schools, conducted curriculum and effectiveness workshops, and established an educational program for residents in a drug rehabilitation facility.

Ms. Murphy became interested in creating a reading series for older students when she began working with adults and adolescents in the early 1970s. The **Challenger Adult Reading Series** is the result of her work with these students.

In a very real sense, the students contributed greatly to the development of this reading series. Their enthusiasm for learning to read and their willingness to work hard provided inspiration, and their many helpful suggestions influenced the content of both the student books and the teacher's manuals.

It is to these students that the **Challenger Adult Reading Series** is dedicated with the hope that others who wish to become good readers will find this reading program both helpful and stimulating.

A special note of gratitude is also extended to Kay Koschnick, Christina Jagger, and Mary Hutchison of New Readers Press for their work and support in guiding this series to completion.

Table of Contents

Lesson 1

The Long and Short Vowels

ā	a	name	save	hate	late		ă	at	am	can	had	and
ē	be	he	me	see	need	feel	ě	yes	let	get	ten	bed	Eddie
ī	I	time	ride	nine	Mike	fire	ĭ	is	if	him	his	did	with
ō	go	so	woke	Jones	hope		ŏ	Bob	job	got	lot	not
ū	rule	rude	tube	use	fuse		ŭ	but	mud	sun	up	us

Words for Study

o'clock	would	said	of
was	friend	to	do
for	the	you	know
Mr.	have	money	park

Bob Is Late

Bob woke up at nine o'clock. He was late for his job. He hoped Mr. Jones would not fire him. Bob got a ride with a friend named Eddie. His friend Eddie did not have a job at the time.

Eddie said to Bob, "Is Mr. Jones going to fire you?"

"I hope not," said Bob. "I hate the job, but I need the money. If I had a lot of money, I would quit."

"If you do get fired, let me know," said Eddie. "Mike is going to the park with me at ten o'clock. You can go with us if you do get fired."

Mr. Jones did fire Bob, so Bob rode to the park with Eddie and Mike.

1 **Read and Write.**

1. The name of Bob's friend is Eddie.

   _____

2. Do you know if he got the job?

   _____

3. Bob and his friends had fun at the park.

   _____

4. Mike did not know the rules, but Eddie did.

   _____

5. Can you save money?

   _____

6. He knows I am not late for the job.

   _____

7. Eddie was in bed at ten o'clock, and the sun woke him up.

   _____

8. Bob did not feel he was rude to Mr. Jones.

   _____

2 **Read and Write.** Note the silent _e_ rule.

time
Tim
   1. _____ did not have _____ to go to the park.

tube
tub
   2. The _____ was in the _____.

not
note
   3. Bob did _____ get a _____ from Mr. Jones.

can
cane
   4. _____ you use a _____?

quit
quite
   5. Bob did not _____, but he was _____ late.

Lesson 2

More Work with Long and Short Vowels

ā	date	gate	lane	take		ă	man	Dan	Dad	bad	
ē	we	keep	meet	week		ě	red	wet	pen	when	
ī	mile	bike	five	hire		ĭ	it	sit	six	fix	which
ō	home	hole	rose	joke		ŏ	cop	box	Mom	God	
ū	tune	duke	huge	cute		ŭ	cup	rub	gum	hug	

Words for Study

on	work	want	around
from	that	down	very
how	relaxed	okay	by
without	until	let's	or

Bob Meets Dan Rose

Bob had a date to see a man named Dan Rose. Mr. Rose had a home on Red Gate Lane, which was six miles from Bob's home. Dan Rose was a friend of Bob's dad, and he had a job for Bob.

The job was fixing bikes. Bob did not know how to fix bikes, but it was so bad to be without a job that he had said to his dad he would take the job.

Bob said to Eddie, "I hope I feel relaxed when I meet Dan. I do not have to see him until five o'clock."

Eddie did not want to let his friend down, so he said, "Okay, let's ride around until it is time to see him."

Bob was very relaxed by the time he got to Dan's home at five o'clock. Dan said he would hire Bob to fix bikes.

1 **Read and Write.**

1. Tim rode five miles on his bike.

_____

2. Eddie and Mike joked with the cop.

_____

3. The duke was quite rude to the man at the gate.

_____

4. Do you know if Mom is feeling okay?

_____

5. Dad said, "You can use the cup if you want to."

_____

6. Bob said that he would be home around six o'clock.

_____

7. The mud was so bad that Mr. Lane did not ride his bike to work.

_____

8. Do you use a pen to do the work?

_____

2 **Read and Write.** Note the silent _e_ rule.

huge _or_ hug 　　1. Mom needed a _____ box for the roses.

cute _or_ cut 　　2. Mike had a bad _____ and had to go home.

meet _or_ met 　　3. Eddie got to the park by six o'clock and _____ his friends.

use _or_ us 　　4. It was so late that Mr. Jones wanted _____ to go home.

cope _or_ cop 　　5. Tim knows that he can _____ with his job.

rode _or_ rod 　　6. We _____ down to Dan's house to see how he was feeling.

hopes _or_ hops 　　7. Bob _____ he can fix the bikes.

ate _or_ at 　　8. "If you want to do the work, you have to keep _____ it," said Dan.

Lesson 3

More Work with Long and Short Vowels

ā	Kate	lake	made	Dave	ă	mad	hat	nap	jab
ē	beep	jeep	seem	seen	ě	men	set	pet	pep
ī	fine	mine	wipe	nice	ĭ	zip	sip	lid	kid
ō	rope	bone	Coke	Pope	ŏ	hot	pot	Tom	rob
ū	June	nude	mule	cube	ŭ	fun	fuss	bus	bug

Words for Study

girlfriend	her	been	then
she	loved	saw	sight
woman	as	horn	off
bank	much	first	one

Eddie's Girlfriend

Eddie's girlfriend was named Kate. Kate worked in a bank. She was cute, and Eddie loved her. He would see her five or six times a week. Eddie hoped that Kate loved him as much as he loved her.

Eddie had met Kate at the lake. He had been with Mike and Dave in Dave's jeep. When Eddie saw Kate, he made Dave beep the horn so she would see him.

At first, Kate seemed mad at the beeping, but then she saw Eddie. It was love at first sight! Eddie and Kate had fun at the lake, and then she rode off with him in Dave's jeep.

1 **Read and Write.**

mad
made
mud

1. Dave got _____ when he saw the _____ on his
jeep, and he _____ Mike wipe it off.

hat
hates
hot

2. When it is _____, the woman _____ to be
without a _____.

sip
six
sit

3. At _____ o'clock, Bob and Eddie _____ by the lake
at the park and _____ Cokes.

cope
cop
cup

4. The _____ did not know how to _____ with the bug
he saw in his _____.

man
men
mine

5. The _____ did not know that five _____ worked
in the _____.

fuse
used
us

6. Not one of _____ knows which _____ is to be
_____.

am
as
at

7. She is as mad _____ Tom _____ I _____.

Kate
late
dates

8. As a rule, Eddie is not _____ for his _____ with
_____.

pen
pet
pep

9. Kate's _____ had so much _____ that she had to keep
her in a _____ when she was working.

2 **Read and Write.** Mark the vowels in these words.

1. fīre̸	3. cane	5. woke	7. hole	9. ate	11. me	13. jab	15. keep
2. sĭp	4. nice	6. sun	8. bed	10. use	12. lid	14. cute	16. rule

Lesson 4

Changing the First Consonant Sound

ā	Dave	made	bake	came		ă	bad	hat	man	nap
	gave	fade	cake	game			fad	fat	pan	lap
	wave	wade	make	tame			sad	pat	tan	cap
ē	week	feel	meet	need		ĕ	bed	let	ten	yes
	peek	heel	beet	feed			fed	bet	den	mess
	seek	reel	feet	seed			led	net	hen	less
ī	quite	ride	bike	time		ĭ	sip	quit	six	win
	bite	side	hike	dime			lip	kit	fix	pin
	kite	wide	like	lime			rip	fit	mix	tin
ō	go	bone	hole	hope		ŏ	rod	pot	Bob	hop
	no	cone	pole	dope			cod	dot	mob	mop
	so	phone	sole	rope			nod	rot	sob	top
ū	tune	rule	use	cube		ŭ	gum	bug	tub	sun
	June	mule	fuse	tube			hum	dug	rub	run
	dune	Yule	refuse				bum	rug	cub	gun

Words for Study

lived	help	last	herself
aunt	this	oven	behind
Louise	out	looked	put
didn't	went	also	should

Kate Bakes a Cake

Kate lived with her aunt. Her aunt's name was Louise. Kate wanted to bake a cake for Eddie, but she didn't know how to bake. Aunt Louise said she would help Kate, but Kate refused her help. She would bake this cake without help!

At last, it was time to take the cake out of the oven. The cake looked like a joke. She ate a bite. It was bad! She fed the cake to the cat. The cat hated the cake also.

Kate was very sad. She was also mad at herself for refusing Aunt Louise's help. She dug a hole behind her home and put the cake in it. She hoped that Aunt Louise didn't see her.

1 Read and Write.

cute *or* cut   1. The kid was so _____ that Aunt Louise gave him a hug.

tube *or* tub   2. Tom was in the _____, so he didn't get to the phone in time.

rode *or* rod   3. Bob used Eddie's _____ and reel at the lake.

Cap *or* Cape   4. Mr. Jones went to _____ Cod.

rip *or* ripe   5. The beet was _____, so Mike ate it.

ride *or* rid   6. Dan said to Bob, "Get _____ of that note. I do not need it."

win *or* wine   7. June likes to sip red _____ when she is relaxing.

fade *or* fad   8. Sitting on top of poles used to be a huge _____.

hop *or* hope   9. "I _____ you like fixing bikes," said Eddie to Bob.

fuse *or* fuss   10. When Aunt Louise saw how sad Kate looked, she said, "Do not make a _____. You should have seen the first cake I made."

led, less, *or* let   11. Dave _____ Eddie use his jeep.

feed, feel, *or* feet   12. Do you _____ like going to the park with me?

hat, hot, *or* hit   13. It was so _____ that Dave didn't go bike riding.

him, hum, *or* ham   14. Aunt Louise baked a _____ for Bob.

fade, feed, *or* fed   15. Kate didn't _____ the cake to her pet.

2 Yes or No.

1. Do you have a bike? _____   6. Can you run a mile? _____

2. Can you bake a cake? _____   7. Have you been for a ride in a jeep? _____

3. Do you have a job? _____   8. Do you like to have lots of friends? _____

4. Can you save money? _____   9. Do you make a mess when you bake? _____

5. Do you like to joke? _____   10. Do you like getting help with this work? _____

Word Index: Lessons 1-4

A
a
also
am
and
around
as
at
ate
aunt

B
bad
bake
bank
be
bed
been
beep
beet
behind
bet
bike
bite
Bob
bone
box
bug
bum
bus
but
by

C
cake
came
can
cane
cap
cape
Cape Cod
cod
Coke
cone
cop
cope

cub
cube
cup
cut
cute

D
dad
Dan
date
Dave
den
did
didn't
dime
do
dope
dot
down
dug
duke
dune

E
Eddie

F
fad
fade
fat
fed
feed
feel
feet
fine
fire
first
fit
five
fix
for
friend
from
fun
fuse
fuss

G
game
gate
gave
get
girlfriend
go
God
got
gum
gun

H
had
hat
hate
have
he
heel
help
hen
her
herself
hike
him
hire
his
hit
hole
home
hop
hope
horn
hot
how
huge
hug
hum

I
I
if
is
it

J
jab
jeep
job
joke
Jones
June

K
Kate
keep
kid
kit
kite
know

L
lake
lane
lap
last
late
led
less
let
let's
lid
like
lime
lip
live
look
lot(s)
Louise
love

M
mad
made
make
man
me
meet
men
mess
met

Mike
mile
mine
mix
mob
mom
money
mop
Mr.
much
mud
mule

N
name
nap
need
net
nice
nine
no
nod
not
note
nude

O
o'clock
of
off
okay
on
one
or
out
oven

P
pan
park
pat
peek
pen
pep
pet
phone

pin
pole
Pope
pot
put

Q
quit
quite

R
red
reel
refuse
relax
rid
ride
rip
ripe
rob
rod
rode
rope
rose
rot
rub
rude
rug
rule
run

S
sad
said
save
saw
see
seed
seek
seem
seen
set
she
should

side
sight
sip
sit
six
so
sob
sole
sun

T
take
tame
tan
ten
that
the
then
this
Tim
time
tin
to
Tom
top
tub
tube
tune

U
until
up
us
use

V
very

W
wade
want
was
wave
we
week
went

wet
when
which
wide
win
wine
wipe
with
without
woman
woke
work
would

X

Y
yes
you
Yule

Z
zip

Lesson 5

Changing the End Consonant Sound

Long vowels	ā	ē	ī	ō	ū
	fade	beet	wine	note	mule
	fame	beep	wife	nose	mute
	face	beef	wire	nope	muse
	cape	week	time	rode	tune
	case	weed	tide	robe	tube
	cage	weep	tire	role	
	safe	seem	line	hole	fuse
	same	seed	life	home	fume
	sale	seep	like	hose	

Short vowels	ă	ĕ	ĭ	ŏ	ŭ
	tan	bed	hit	cod	hum
	tap	bet	hip	cop	hug
	tax	Ben	hid	cot	hut
	jab	pep	mix	Mom	bug
	jam	pen	miss	mop	bun
	jazz	pet	mitt	mob	bud
	ran	wet	bit	pot	sum
	rat	web	big	pop	sub
	ram	wed	bib	pod	suds

Words for Study

talk	something	women	year
after	problem	who	don't
dinner	it's	Mrs.	about
ask	call	Ms.	other

Talking with Aunt Louise

Aunt Louise was Kate's aunt. She was also a woman Kate's friends liked to talk to. Bob went to see Aunt Louise after work. She was fixing beef for dinner.

"Can I ask you something, Aunt Louise?" asked Bob. "I have a problem at work, and I need help."

"But you said that you liked the job," said Aunt Louise.

"I do like it," Bob said. "It's not a big problem. The problem is that I don't know if I should call the women who need bikes fixed Miss, Mrs., or Ms. I bet talking was a lot safer when men and women had the same roles year after year."

"Don't bet on it," said Aunt Louise. "Year after year, men and women get worked up about something or other. Would you like to have dinner with us?"

"Yes," said Bob, "I would love to."

It was fun to talk and joke with Aunt Louise.

1 **Read and Write.** Add *-ed* to these words.

1. look + ed = *looked*

2. last + ed = _____

3. talk + ed = _____

4. ask + ed = _____

5. mess + ed = _____

6. relax + ed = _____

1. face + ed = *faced*

2. save + ed = _____

3. joke + ed = _____

4. hire + ed = _____

5. line + ed = _____

6. refuse + ed = _____

1. hop + ed = *hopped*

2. sip + ed = _____

3. pat + ed = _____

4. gun + ed = _____

5. pop + ed = _____

6. sob + ed = _____

2 **Read and Write.**

bone, cone, *or* phone   1. If you want to talk, you can call a friend on the _____.

bug, bum *or* bus   2. If you need a ride, you can take a _____.

safe, sale, *or* save   3. June wanted a robe, so she went to a _____.

bad, bed, *or* bud   4. A cot is a _____.

pan, pen, *or* pin   5. To bake a cake, you need a _____.

red, rid, *or* rod   6. Ben looked at the beet and saw it was _____.

came, cane, *or* cage   7. If he cuts his heel, he can use a _____.

hit, hot, *or* hut   8. A duke would not want to live in a _____.

bone, cone, *or* phone   9. After dinner, Dave gave his pet a _____.

bugs, hugs, *or* rugs   10. Aunt Louise loved Kate and gave her lots of _____.

hope, horn, *or* hose   11. Mrs. Jones likes jazz very much, and she is saving her money for a _____.

game, name, *or* tame   12. Dan didn't know Aunt Louise's last _____.

pat, peek, *or* park   13. Mr. Jones refused to take his wife to the _____.

lap, nap, *or* tap   14. When you sit down, you make a _____.

Lesson 6

Ending Consonant Blends

nd	and	end	bind	bond	fund
	band	bend	find	fond	funds
	hand	lend	kind	pond	refund
	land	mend	mind		
	sand	send	remind		

nt	ant	bent	hint	don't	bunt
	can't	dent	lint	won't	hunt
	pant	sent	mint		punt
	pants	rent			runt

ck	back	deck	kick	hock	buck
	quack	neck	pick	lock	duck
	sack	peck	quick	rock	luck
	tack		sick	sock	lucky
	track				

mp	damp		limp		bump
	lamp				dump
	ramp				jump
					pump

Words for Study

maybe	next	happy	himself
could	won	again	walked
few	what	wasn't	town
there	good	horse	robber

Eddie's Luck

Eddie wanted to get his girlfriend Kate a box of red roses, but he didn't have the money. His friends didn't have the money to lend him, so he hopped on a bus and went to the track. Maybe he could pick up a few bucks there.

When Eddie got to the track, the woman next to him was kind. She gave Eddie a few hints on betting. He bet the money he had and won. Eddie was so happy that he jumped up and down, bumping the men and women around him.

Eddie made up his mind to bet again. He won again. What good luck! He could buy roses for Kate, a box of mints for his mom, and some pants for himself.

Eddie made up his mind to bet again. This time he wasn't so lucky. His horse limped in last, and that was the end of Eddie's money.

1 **Read and Write.** Add *-ed* to these words.

1. call + ed = _called_

2. hunt + ed = _____

3. land + ed = _____

4. walk + ed = _____

5. dump + ed = _____

6. mend + ed = _____

1. bake + ed = _baked_

2. name + ed = _____

3. like + ed = _____

4. date + ed = _____

5. tire + ed = _____

6. hope + ed = _____

1. rob + ed = _robbed_

2. kid + ed = _____

3. rip + ed = _____

4. net + ed = _____

5. top + ed = _____

6. ram + ed = _____

2 Read and Write.

sack, sick, *or* sock

1. The robber was _____ of being on the run. He wanted to go home.

bent, sent, *or* rent

2. The duke _____ ten men to find the robber.

bunt, hunt, *or* runt

3. The men had been on a _____ for the robber for five weeks.

damp, lamp, *or* ramp

4. It was so _____ out that the men got quite wet.

bucked, ducked, *or* lucked

5. The robber _____ behind the rocks to keep out of sight.

band, hand, *or* sand

6. A woman walked by, but she would not lend the robber a _____.

kick, pick, *or* sick

7. The robber was so mad that he wanted to _____ her.

bond, fond, *or* pond

8. The duke's men picked up the robber by a _____.

dent, rent, *or* sent

9. The men gave the woman money and _____ her back to town.

deck, neck, *or* peck

10. The duke's men put the robber's _____ in a rope.

bend, end, *or* send

11. That was the _____ of the robber.

Lesson 7

More Work with Ending Consonant Blends

ang	ing	ong	ung
bang	king	gong	hung
fang	ring	long	lung
hang	sing	song	rung
rang	wing	wrong	sung
sang	thing	Ping-Pong	

ank	ink	onk	unk
bank	ink	honk	bunk
rank	pink		dunk
sank	sink		funk
tank	wink		junk
thank	think		sunk

Words for Study

clock	new	cat	outside
day	car	into	dozed
downtown	all	left	once

The Wrong Side of the Bed

The clock rang, and Dave woke up in a funk. He wanted to sink back into the bed, but he had to get to the bank by nine o'clock. Dave had the day off from work, and he needed to take money out of the bank so he could go downtown and look for a new car. He didn't want a new car, but he had junked his jeep and didn't like taking the bus to work.

Dave was all set to go when his cat, who was in the jam again, banged into a box of fuses that Dave had left out on the sink. The jam pot hit the sink with a bang, and bits of the pot cut Dave's face. There was also jam on his new pants.

"What a day this is going to be!" said a very mad Dave to the cat. "It's no use going out when you get up on the wrong side of the bed."

Dave wiped up the jam, kicked the cat outside, went back to bed, and dozed off at once.

1 **Read and Write.** Add *-ing* to these words.

1. go   + ing = _going_

2. fix   + ing = _____

3. sing + ing = _____

4. look + ing = _____

5. miss + ing = _____

1. take + ing = _taking_

2. have + ing = _____

3. bake + ing = _____

4. joke + ing = _____

5. hope + ing = _____

1. run + ing = _running_

2. sip   + ing = _____

3. pat   + ing = _____

4. jab   + ing = _____

5. hop + ing = _____

2 **Read and Write.** Use the rule you know for the new words.

cat, fat, *or* sat   1. Aunt Louise _____ on the tacks that Kate had left on her bed.

den, hen, *or* ten   2. She was as mad as a wet _____.

big, dig, *or* pig   3. Dave ate like a _____ and then he got sick.

bone, cone, *or* zone   4. The man didn't get hit until he was in the end _____.

hat, mat, *or* rat   5. A _____ was living in a hole behind Bob's bed.

hide, side, *or* wide   6. Dave woke up on the wrong _____ of the bed.

dot, hot, *or* jot   7. Bob said that he would meet Mike at five o'clock on the

_____.

cuts, huts, *or* nuts   8. Kate hoped that if she put a cup of _____ in the cake, it would not be so bad.

sale, male, *or* pale   9. Ms. Bond had been sick for a week, and her face was quite

_____.

dump, jump, *or* pump   10. Bob put the junk in his car, so he could take it to the

_____.

mile, file, *or* pile   11. Kate had to _____ the notes from the meeting at the bank.

peck, pick, *or* pack   12. Eddie did not _____ a good horse to bet on at the track.

lamp, limp, *or* lump   13. When Kate got the cake out of the oven, it looked like a

big _____.

find, fond, *or* fund   14. Mr. Jones was very _____ of his wife.

band, bend, *or* bind   15. The other day, Mrs. Jones went to see a jazz _____.

Lesson 8

Review of Vowels and Consonants

fāce	sāle	cāge	lāke	jăb	păck	căt
race	pale	page	fake	cab	Jack	bat
lace	tale	wage	rake	dab	lack	fat
pace	male	rage	wake	lab	Mack	mat
ace	female	age	awake	tab	rack	sat

fēel	bĕnt	nīce	fīle	dĭg	kĭck
peel	went	rice	mile	pig	Dick
heel	tent	mice	pile	wig	nick
keel	lent	dice	tile	rig	tick
eel	cent	ice	while	fig	lick

phōne	jōke	lŏck		ūse	bŭg
zone	Coke	dock		fuse	jug
tone	poke	hock		refuse	lug
lone	woke	mock		amuse	mug
alone	awoke	rock		amusement	tug

Words for Study

never	my	some	just
an	were	done	here
they	where	ago	will
your	over	stayed	now

At the Amusement Park

Aunt Louise had never been to an amusement park. One day she talked her good friend Jack into going to one with her. As they rode in the cab, Jack said, "At your age, I can't see how you have never been to an amusement park."

"What do you think my age is?" Aunt Louise asked. She was getting mad. Jack didn't want her to make a fuss, so they talked about the fun they would have.

Once they were at the amusement park, Aunt Louise was happy again. She loved the rides and the games. She also liked the huge tents where she and Jack ate and ate until they just about keeled over. Then Jack said that they should go home while they had some money left.

"It seems as if we just got here!" said Aunt Louise.

"You should have done this years ago," said Jack. "The rides were ten cents then, and we could have stayed longer."

"In that case, let's stay," said Aunt Louise. "Who knows how much money it will take to go to an amusement park a year from now."

"Okay," said Jack. It was no use talking Aunt Louise out of something once she had made up her mind.

1 **Read and Write.** Use the rules you know for the new words.

rode *or* code
1. Do you know your zip _____?

box *or* fox
2. The _____ hid in a hole until the man with a gun left.

ram, ham, *or* dam
3. At the meeting, the men and women said that the _____ needed to be fixed at once, or the town would have a big problem.

bad, pad, *or* add
4. Ben jotted down the note on a _____ by the phone.

five, live, *or* dive
5. Eddie liked to go to the lake and _____ from the dock.

fame, tame, *or* lame
6. Ms. Bond wanted to _____ a fox and keep it for a pet.

date, mate, *or* rate
7. At the _____ Kate was working, she would never make the meeting on time.

lined, dined, *or* pined
8. Mr. and Mrs. Jones _____ at six o'clock.

2 **Read and Write.** Use *a* or *an* in these sentences.

1. Tim was very happy when he landed _____ eel in his net.

2. My cat had _____ dab of mud on her face.

3. Mack used _____ mat to wipe his feet.

4. Dan said to Eddie that he had _____ outside phone call.

5. Tom used _____ ice cube to get the gum off the rug.

6. The duck quacked again and again when _____ gun was fired.

7. Aunt Louise won _____ pink mug at the amusement park.

8. When Bob had _____ problem, he liked to talk with Aunt Louise.

9. The rope put _____ end to the robber's life.

10. Aunt Louise was at _____ age when she wanted to do all the things she had never done in her life.

3 **Read and Write.** Mark the vowels.

1. fūmé   6. hand   11. mind

2. lĕss   7. sock   12. refuse

3. neck   8. safe   13. us

4. robe   9. quick   14. beef

5. tick   10. cent   15. female

4 **Read and Write.** Match the words that mean the same thing.

fix   _huge_   1. big
six   _____   2. save
seek   _____   3. look for
weep   _____   4. beep
keep   _____   5. five and one
fun   _____   6. poke
females   _____   7. mend
honk   _____   8. amusement
✓ huge   _____   9. sob
jab   _____   10. women

5 **Read and Write.** Answer these questions in good sentence form.

New words: them   are   quickly

1. When it is time to quit, do you relax or keep on working?

_____

2. Do you like to go out on the town, or do you like to be at home?

_____

3. Do you fix things that don't work, or do you get rid of them?

_____

4. Do your friends think that you are happy or sad?

_____

5. Do you take time on a job, or do you work very quickly?

_____

6. Do you have lots of pep when you wake up, or do you feel tired?

_____

7. Did you fix the last dinner you made in a pot or a pan?

_____

8. Are you late for your dates, or do you get there on time?

_____

9. Do you ask for help when you need it, or do you like to do all your work alone?

_____

10. Do you like to phone your friends, or do you like to see them face to face?

_____

Word Index: Lessons 1-8

A
a
about
ace
add
after
again
age
ago
all
alone
also
am
amuse
amusement
an
and
ant
are
around
as
ask
at
ate
aunt
awake
awoke

B
back
bad
bake
band
bang
bank
bat
be
bed
beef
been
beep
beet
behind
Ben
bend
bent
bet
bib
big
bike
bind
bit

bite
Bob
boil
bond
bone
box
buck
bud
bug
bum
bump
bun
bunk
bunt
bus
but
by

C
cab
cage
cake
call
came
can
cane
can't
cap
cape
Cape Cod
car
case
cat
cent
clock
cod
code
Coke
cone
cop
cope
cot
could
cub
cube
cup
cut
cute

D
dab
dad

dam
damp
Dan
date
Dave
day
deck
den
dent
dice
Dick
did
didn't
dig
dime
dine
diner
dinner
dive
do
dock
done
don't
dope
dot
down
downtown
doze
duck
dug
duke
dump
dune
dunk

E
Eddie
eel
end

F
face
fad
fade
fake
fame
fang
fat
fed
fee
feed

feel
feet
female
few
fig
file
find
fine
fire
first
fit
five
fix
fond
for
fox
friend
from
fume
fun
fund(s)
funk
funny
fuse
fuss

G
game
gate
gave
get
girlfriend
go
God
gong
good
got
gum
gun

H
had
ham
hand
hang
happy
hat
hate
have
he
heel

help
hen
her
here
herself
hid
hide
hike
him
himself
hint
hip
hire
his
hit
hock
hole
home
honk
hop
hope
horn
horse
hose
hot
how
hug
huge
hum
hung
hunt
hut

I
I
ice
if
in
ink
into
is
it
it's

J
jab
Jack
jack
jam
jazz
jeep

job
joke
Jones
jot
jug
jump
June
junk
just

K
Kate
keel
keep
kick
kid
kind
king
kit
kite
know

L
lab
lace
lack
lake
lame
lamp
land
lane
lap
last
late
led
left
lend
lent
less
let
let's
lick
lid
life
like
lime
limp
line
lint
lip
live
lock
long

lone
look
lot(s)
Louise
love
luck
lucky
lug
lump
lung

M
Mack
mad
made
make
male
man
mat
mate
maybe
me
meet
meeting
men
mend
mess
met
mice
Mike
mile
mind
mine
mint
miss
mitt
mix
mob
mock
mom
money
mop
Mr.
Mrs.
Ms.
much
mud
mug
mule
muse
mute
my

N
name
nap
neck
need
net
never
new
next
nice
nick
nine
no
nod
nope
nose
not
note
now
nude
nut

O
o'clock
of
off
okay
on
once
one
or
other
out
outside
oven
over

P
pace
pack
pad
page
pale
pan
pant
pants
park
pat
peck
peek
peel

pen
pep
pet
phone
pick
pig
pile
pin
pine
Ping-Pong
pink
pod
poke
pole
pond
pop
Pope
pot
problem
pump
punt
put

Q
quack
quick
quickly
quit
quite

R
race
rack
rage
rake
ram
ramp
ran
rang
rank
rat
rate
red
reel
refund
refuse
relax
remind
rent
rice
rid
ride

rig
ring
rip
ripe
rob
robber
robe
rock
rod
rode
role
rope
rose
rot
rub
rude
rug
rule
run
rung
runt

S
sack
sad
safe
said
sale
same
sand
sang
sank
sat
save
saw
see
seed
seek
seem
seen
seep
send
sent
set
she
should
sick
side
sight
sing
sink
sip

sit
six
so
sob
sock
sole
some
something
song
stay
sub
suds
sum
sun
sung
sunk

T
tab
tack
take
tale
talk
tame
tan
tank
tap
tax
ten
tent
thank
that
the
them
then
there
they
thing
think
this
tick
tide
tile
Tim
time
tin
tire
to
Tom
tone
top
town

track
tub
tube
tug
tune

U
until
up
us
use

V
very

W
wade
wage
wake
walk
want
was
wasn't
wave
we
web
wed
weed
week
weep
went
were
wet
what
when
where
which
while
who
wide
wife
wig
will
win
wine
wing
wink
wipe
wire

with
without
woke
woman
women
won
won't
work
would
wrong

X

Y
year
yes
you
your
Yule

Z
zip
zone

Lesson 9

Vowel Sounds for *y*

y:	my	myself	cry	try	sky	why	
ay:	day	may	pay	payment	play	say	way
ey:	key	monkey	donkey				
oy:	boy	joy	toy	Roy	royal	loyal	
uy:	buy	guy					

day	**Days of the week**
today	Sunday
yesterday	Monday
birthday	Tuesday
payday	Wednesday
	Thursday
	Friday
	Saturday

Words for Study

none	please	only	little
any	hurt	since	what's
party	yet	Linda	funny

A Birthday Party for Bob

Wednesday was Bob's birthday, and his friends wanted to buy him something nice. Payday wasn't until Friday, and none of Bob's friends had any money.

Kate said she would bake the cake for the party, but Eddie said, "No, please don't. Let your aunt bake the cake. She said that she would. Why don't you pick up some wine on your way home from the bank?"

Kate was so hurt that she wanted to cry, but she said, "Okay, but next time, I want to bake the cake."

Bob's friends didn't know what to buy for him yet. They had only six bucks to get something nice. Dave said, "Since we don't have any money, why don't we play a joke on Bob and buy him some toys?"

Linda got mad at Dave. "Bob is not a little boy, you know. He is going to be 24 on Wednesday. What's he going to do with a lot of toys?"

Dave said, "Bob will think it's funny. Let's do it." So they all got into Mike's car and went downtown to buy Bob some toys for his birthday.

All the way downtown, Linda said to herself, "I think I am out of my mind to be going out to buy toys for a man's birthday."

1 Read and Write.

1. mess   + y = _messy_
2. fuss   + y = _____
3. bump + y = _____
4. need   + y = _____
5. robber + y = _____

1. ice   + y = _icy_
2. nose + y = _____
3. lace   + y = _____
4. bone + y = _____
5. wire   + y = _____

1. fun   + y = _funny_
2. sun   + y = _____
3. Mom + y = _____
4. Dad   + y = _____
5. nut   + y = _____

2 **Read and Write.** Note that the words at the left end in *-ly*.
Use these words in the five sentences.

friendly
lovely
safely
weekly
quickly

1. Mr. Jones did his work _____ on Tuesday so he would have time to buy his wife a new robe for her birthday.

2. Yesterday, Mrs. Jones looked up at the sky and said,

   "What a _____ day this is!"

3. "Don't fuss so much," said Aunt Louise to Kate. "I can get home _____ by myself."

4. Kate was happy working at the bank. The others who worked there were

   so _____ to her.

5. Bob had lent quite a lot of money to Dave for his new car. Dave said he would

   pay him back in _____ payments.

3 **Read and Write.** More words that end with *y*.

> Note: The *y* is changed to *i* in these words.
> cry   cries   cried
> try   tries   tried
> Read these words in the sentences below.

baby (bā-by)   1. The ___*baby*___ cries when his mom tries to put on his bib.

candy (căn-dy)   2. Dave gave Linda a huge box of _____.

sixty (sĭx-ty)   3. Bob's dad was _____ when he quit his job.

lobby (lŏb-by)   4. Eddie met Kate in the _____ at five o'clock.

ninety (nīne-ty)   5. There were _____ women at the meeting yesterday.

Andy (Ăn-dy)   6. _____ tried to buy Bob a kite for his birthday, but there were none left.

muddy (mŭd-dy)   7. The baby cried when he landed in the _____ hole.

handy (hănd-y)   8. Roy was so _____ that he fixed the sink in no time.

forty (for-ty)   9. When Jack takes a nap, he calls it "getting _____ winks."

Bucky (Bŭck-y)   10. The king sat down to the royal dinner next to his loyal friend,

   _____.

4 **Read and Write.** Match the words that mean the same thing.

Sunday
joke   _____   1. to keep out of sight
hide
not happy   _____   2. in back of
jack
male   _____   3. a dime
ten cents   _____   4. man
refuse
Saturday   _____   5. sad
behind
funny   _____   6. to make fun of
mock
                    _____   7. to kid around

                    _____   8. to say *no*

                    _____   9. amusing

                    _____   10. you use this to fix a tire

                    _____   11. the first day of the week

                    _____   12. the last day of the week

Lesson 10

Silent Letters

kn	wr	mb	ight	tch	tch
know	wrong	lamb	sight	catch	itch
known	wrap	climb	fight	match	ditch
knew	wreck	bomb	light	batch	witch
knee	write	dumb	might	patch	
knife	wrote	numb	night		Dutch
knot	wrist	thumb	right	fetch	
knock			tight	ketchup	

Words for Study

gone	street	act	gas
movie	front	swung	too
middle	still	foot	sadly

Eddie's Night Out

Eddie had gone downtown to meet Kate. They had a date to see a movie. As Eddie was sitting in the car at a red light, a man came up to him and said, "Do you have a match?"

Eddie said, "Look, man, this is the middle of a street. Get out of the way."

This made the man mad. He got out a knife and waved it in front of Eddie's face. "I said, do you have a match?"

Eddie was numb. He knew he didn't have a match. He also knew this guy was just a bum looking for a fight. What was wrong with the light? Why was it still red?

Eddie knew he had to act quickly. He swung his right hand around and, with all his might, knocked the knife from the man's hand.

Eddie was so happy that he was safe that he put his foot on the gas too quickly and ended up wrapping the car around a pole. He climbed out of the ditch he had landed in. His knee was banged up, so he was limping a little bit.

"All I hoped for was to have a nice time with Kate. I wanted to see a movie, not feel as if I have been in one," said Eddie sadly to himself as he looked at the wrecked car and rubbed his banged-up knee.

1   **Read and Write.** Use the rules you know for the new words.

gas
pass

1. Knowing that he needed _____ at once, Ben didn't _____ the car in front of him.

acts
fact

2. It is a _____ that Bucky is called a baby only when he _____ like one.

one
none
done

3. _____ of the women had to bake any cakes for the party since _____ man had _____ all the baking.

knew
new
few

4. Linda _____ that a _____ of the women at the party were _____ in town.

lights
right
night

5. Aunt Louise was _____ when she said that having all the _____ on would help Jack stay awake at _____ while he worked on his taxes.

see
knee
fee

6. Eddie could _____ that he would have to pay quite a big _____ to have the cut on his _____ and the car fixed.

note
wrote
vote

7. Andy _____ a _____ to Roy in which he asked him to _____ for Tom at the meeting.

neck
wreck
heck

8. "What the _____," said Eddie. "I should be happy that I didn't hurt my _____ in the _____."

locked
dock
knock

9. Aunt Louise had left her keys down at the _____ and was _____ out. She had to _____ ten times, and then Kate came to let her in.

day
way
lay

10. When Ms. Bond _____ down last night, she hoped that she could find her _____ downtown by herself the next _____.

2 **Opposites.** Pick the word that means the opposite, and write it on the line.

back	_night_	1. day
bad	_____	2. first
huge	_____	3. front
last	_____	4. good
✓ night	_____	5. happy
play	_____	6. little
sad	_____	
same	_____	7. right
there	_____	8. work
wrong	_____	9. here
	_____	10. opposite

3 **Word Study.** Pick the word that does not fit with the rest and write it on the line.

1. Monday	Friday	Thursday	yesterday	_yesterday_
2. aunt	dad	friend	mom	_____
3. bus	cab	car	foot	_____
4. ant	cat	donkey	monkey	_____
5. day	sun	week	year	_____
6. boy	females	guy	man	_____
7. buns	cakes	candy	wine	_____
8. crying	fussy	mad	numb	_____
9. cot	home	hut	tent	_____
10. fit	hat	pants	robe	_____

Lesson 11

The r-Controlled Vowels

ar:	car	card	arm	harm	dark	part	start
are:	care	bare	dare	fare	rare		
or:	horse	more	morning	fork	sort	lord	
er:	her	herd	jerk	nerve	serve	verse	
eer:	beer	deer	peer	queer			
ir:	girl	dirt	birthday	birth	firm	firmly	
ur:	hurt	turn	burn	burp	curve	purse	

Words for Study

pretzels	because	sorry	yourself	there's
door	thought	always	I'm	lose
Mary	felt	come	says	laughed

The Card Game

Jack and Eddie were playing cards over at Aunt Louise's. Aunt Louise had just served some beer and pretzels when there was a knock on the front door. It was Mary, a girl who lived down the street. She asked if she could stay with Aunt Louise for a while. Her mom and dad had not come home from work yet, and she didn't like being alone because it was just starting to get dark.

Mary was ten. She had dirt all over her face and arms from playing hide-and-seek. Eddie had always thought Mary was sort of queer, but he felt sorry for her. Her mom and dad always got home so late from work.

"It's good to see you, Mary," said Aunt Louise. "Go wipe yourself off at the sink, and then you can sit with us. Can I get you a Coke?"

"Yes, thank you," said Mary. "Can I play cards, too? I'm very lucky at cards, my dad says."

Jack said he didn't like having little girls around when he played cards. They gave him bad luck. Eddie said that he didn't care. Aunt Louise was quite happy that Mary had come. She said in a firm tone to Jack, "With Mary here, I think tonight is going to be my lucky night."

While they were playing, Mary said, "Can I have some beer, too?"

"Cards, yes. Beer, no," said Aunt Louise firmly.

"Okay," said Mary. "Like my dad says, there's no harm in asking."

Mary played cards with them until it was time for her to go home. Aunt Louise and Mary won just about all the hands. Jack hated to lose, so he didn't have a very good time that night. He was mad when Mary left. "The nerve of that girl," said Jack. "She comes in here and has Coke and all the pretzels, wins just about all the hands, and then runs off just when I'm starting to feel lucky."

Aunt Louise and Eddie just sat there and laughed.

1 **Read and Write.** Add -er to these words.

1. quick + er = _quicker_

1. fine + er = _finer_

2. tight + er = _____

2. rude + er = _____

3. few + er = _____

3. cute + er = _____

4. box + er = _____

4. bake + er = _____

5. hunt + er = _____

5. late + er = _____

6. burn + er = _____

6. dine + er = _____

1. big + er = _bigger_

2. fat + er = _____

3. hot + er = _____

4. win + er = _____

5. hit + er = _____

6. mug + er = _____

2 **Read and Write.** More words that end in er.

bumper (bŭmp-er) 1. On Saturday morning, Tim fixed the dents in his _bumper_ .

hammer (hăm-mer) 2. He used a _____ to bang out the dents.

copper (cŏp-per) 3. _____ was once used to make pennies.

summer (sŭm-mer) 4. Linda is saving her money to go to Cape Cod for the

_____.

pepper (pĕp-per) 5. Dave put red _____ on his rice to make it hotter.

ruler (rūl-er) 6. Mack could not get the lines right because he didn't have a

_____.

worker (work-er) 7. The _____ was sent home in the morning because he felt sick.

better (bĕt-ter) 8. The _____ Bob did his job, the _____ he felt about himself.

46   Lesson 11

3 **Read and Write.** Change the *y* to *i* and add *-er*.

handy _*handier*_   lucky _____   fussy _____

happy _____   lovely _____   bumpy _____

New word: than

Use the words ending in *-ier* for these sentences.

1. Dan was _____ in getting a ride to work than he thought he would be.

2. Mr. Jones was much _____ once his taxes were out of the way.

3. He said to his wife, "You look _____ than you did on the day I first met you."

4. The baby was always _____ when she first woke up from her morning nap.

5. "Don't you think this lane is a lot _____ than it was last summer?" Ms. Bond asked her friend.

6. Bob was a lot _*handier*_ when he was fixing bikes than when he was fixing cars.

4 **Read and Write.** Who does what?

a banker   _*a hunter*_   1. Who uses a gun?

a fighter

✓ a hunter   _____   2. Who uses a pen?

a joker   _____   3. Who knows a lot of songs?

a player

a singer   _____   4. Who kids around a lot and likes to make you laugh?

a thinker

a writer

_____   5. Who keeps your money for you or lends you some money when you need it?

_____   6. Who boxes in a ring and hopes he is not knocked out?

_____   7. Who acts in plays or plays in a game?

_____   8. Who uses his mind and has lots of thoughts?

Lesson 12

Vowel Combinations

ai	ea	ea	ie	oa	ue
aid	eat	dead	die	boat	due
paid	meat	head	lie	soap	dues
mail	tea	lead	pie	coat	Sue
rain	clean	read	tie	goal	blue
wait	read			load	true

oi	oo	oo	ou
oil	food	foot	loud
boil	mood	book	loudly
join	room	cook	house
joint	soon	look	count
voice	zoo	wood	shout

Words for Study

gotten	stopped	well	that's	hear
all right	water	aren't	celebrate	lost
kiss	you're	temper	what's	enough

The Fight

Kate was a happy woman, but she was in a bad mood today. She had not gotten any mail for a week. She needed a new coat, but she didn't have the money to buy one. The house was a mess, but she didn't feel like cleaning it.

Kate fixed herself a cup of tea and waited for Eddie. He was due very soon. What would Eddie think of the messy house? Kate didn't care. Eddie's home was a mess all the time, so Kate thought it was all right if her house looked messy now and then.

Then Eddie came into the room. He was so happy that he was humming a tune in a very loud voice. He was just about to kiss Kate when he saw how messy the room looked and how sad Kate was.

He stopped humming and said, "You do know what soap and water are for, don't you? And why are you in a bad mood?"

Kate counted to ten and then shouted, "Look, if you're going to pick a fight, you can go right back home. I am in no mood to put up with your bad temper right now."

Eddie said, "Okay. I'm going over to Bob's house. Maybe he will celebrate my new job with me."

"A new job!" said Kate. "Eddie, I'm sorry I lost my temper. I don't know what's gotten into me."

"That's okay. I'm too happy to be mad. Come on, let's celebrate and go out to eat," said Eddie.

"I can't wait to hear about the job," Kate said. "And, again, I'm so sorry I shouted at you."

"Sorry enough to pay for the dinner?" joked Eddie.

"Well," Kate said, "not that sorry."

1 **Read and Write.** Fill in the blank with the right word.

boiled
eat
five
fork
house
meat
mug
night
soap
water
work
tea

It was _____ o'clock, and Kate had gotten home from

_____ . Aunt Louise had gone over to Jack's _____ for dinner.

Kate knew she would feel better after she had something to _____ .

She got out some _____ that was left over from last night and

_____ some water for tea. She put the _____ in a

_____ and ate the meat with a _____ .

When she was done, she soaked all the things she had used in _____

and _____ and went over to Linda's house for the _____ .

2 Read and Write.

deer *or* door
1. The men hunted for _____ all day. When they could not find any, they gave up and went home.

read *or* road
2. The _____ was so bumpy that five men had to be hired to fix it.

die *or* due
3. The rent was _____ in one week.

car *or* far
4. Mr. Jones knew he was lost, but he said, "Well, I came this _____. I can't quit looking for the right street now."

barn *or* burn
5. Sue wanted to know who had let the horses out of the _____.

aids *or* ails
6. Eddie said to Kate, "What _____ you?"

lead *or* load
7. "Aren't you going to help me take this _____ of junk to the dump?" asked Mrs. Jones. "It's too much for me to do alone."

pies *or* peas
8. Aunt Louise got out a can of _____ to serve with the meat for dinner.

soak *or* seek
9. Do you _____ your feet in hot water when they hurt?

mood *or* moon
10. It was so dark that Jack used the light of the _____ to find the right key for the back door.

pain *or* paid
11. The _____ in Mike's head was so bad that he wanted to cry.

foot *or* food
12. Eddie put his _____ on the gas too quickly and banged into the car in front of him.

mood *or* maid
13. Kate looked at her messy house and said, "If only I had a _____."

read *or* real
14. Dave was a _____ fighter, but he would only fight if he felt he had to.

house *or* mouse
15. Mr. Jones cried out when he saw a little _____ run right over his foot.

coals *or* coats
16. The _____ died down, and the fire went out.

mail *or* main
17. Ms. Hope didn't like living on the _____ street in her town.

dart *or* dirt   18. The little boys liked to play in the huge pile of _____ at the dump.

bored *or* bared   19. Aunt Louise thought that, since life had been so good to her, she had no right to feel _____.

hard *or* herd   20. Do you think this work is _____?

3   **Read and Write.**

1. Do you like it better when the sun is out or when the moon is out?

_____

2. Do you think that movies are boring, or do you like going to them now and then?

_____

3. When you ride on the bus, do you like to sit in the front or the back?

_____

4. Can you keep a tune, or do you sing off key?

_____

5. Do you write with your right hand or your left hand?

_____

6. When the roads are icy, do you go out, or do you stay at home?

_____

7. Do you start your day by having something to eat, or do you wait until you have been up for a while?

_____

8. Do you lose your temper when things seem to go wrong, or do you try to stay relaxed?

_____

9. Do you think that knowing how to read helps you or hurts you in setting your goals?

_____

Word Index: Lessons 1-12

A
a
about
ace
act
add
after
again
age
ago
aid
ail
all
all right
alone
also
always
am
amuse
amusement
an
and
Andy
ant
any
are
aren't
around
arm
as
ask
at
ate
aunt
awake
awoke

B
baby
back
bad
bake
baker
band
bang
bank
banker
bare
barn
bat
batch
be
because
bed
beef
been
beep
beer
beet

behind
Ben
bend
bent
bet
better
bib
big
bike
bind
birth
birthday
bit
bite
blue
boat
Bob
boil
bomb
bond
bone
bony
book
bore
box
boxer
boy
buck
Bucky
bud
bug
bum
bump
bumper
bumpy
bun
bunk
bunt
burn
burner
burp
bus
but
buy
by

C
cab
cage
cake
call
came
can
candy
cane
can't
cap
cape
Cape Cod

car
card
care
case
cat
catch
celebrate
cent
clean
climb
clock
coal
coat
cod
code
Coke
come
cone
cook
cop
cope
copper
cot
could
count
cry
cub
cube
cup
curve
cut
cute

D
dab
dad
daddy
dam
damp
Dan
dare
dark
dart
date
Dave
day
dead
deck
den
dent
deer
dice
Dick
did
didn't
die
dig
dime
dine

diner
dinner
dirt
ditch
dive
do
dock
done
donkey
don't
door
dope
dot
down
downtown
doze
duck
due
dues
dug
duke
dumb
dump
dune
dunk
Dutch

E
eat
Eddie
eel
end
enough

F
face
fact
fad
fade
fake
fame
fang
far
fare
fat
fed
fee
feed
feel
feet
felt
female
fetch
few
fig
fight
fighter
file
find
fine

fire
firm
firmly
first
fit
five
fix
fond
food
foot
for
fork
forty
fox
Friday
friend
friendly
from
front
fume
fun
fund(s)
funk
funny
fuse
fuss
fussy

G
game
gas
gate
gave
get
girl
girlfriend
go
goal
God
gone
gong
good
got
gotten
gum
gun
guy

H
had
ham
hammer
hand
handy
hang
happy
hard
harm
hat

hate
have
he
head
hear
heck
heel
help
hen
her
herd
here
herself
hid
hide
hide-and-seek
hike
him
himself
hint
hip
hire
his
hit
hitter
hock
hole
home
honk
hop
hope
horn
horse
hose
hot
house
how
hug
huge
hum
hung
hunt
hunter
hurt
hut

I
I
ice
icy
if
I'm
in
ink
into
is
it
itch
it's

J
jab
Jack
jack
jam
jazz
jeep
jerk
job
join
joint
joke
joker
Jones
jot
joy
jug
jump
June
junk
just

K
Kate
keel
keep
ketchup
key
kick
kid
kind
king
kiss
kit
kite
knee
knife
knew
knock
know
known

L
lab
lace
lack
lacy
lake
lamb
lame
lamp
land
lane
lap
last
late
later
laugh
lay

lead
led
left
lend
lent
less
let
let's
lick
lid
lie
life
light
like
lime
limp
Linda
line
lint
lip
little
live
load
lobby
lock
lone
long
look
lord
lose
lost
lot(s)
loud
loudly
Louise
love
lovely
loyal
luck
lucky
lug
lump
lung

M
Mack
mad
made
maid
mail
main
make
male
man
Mary
mat
match
mate
may

maybe
me
meat
meet
meeting
men
mend
mess
messy
met
mice
middle
might
Mike
mile
mind
mine
mint
miss
mitt
mix
mob
mock
mom
mommy
Monday
money
monkey
mood
moon
mop
more
morning
mouse
movie
Mr.
Mrs.
Ms.
much
mud
muddy
mug
mugger
mule
muse
mute
my
myself

N

name
nap
neck
need
needy
nerve
net
never
new
next
nice
nick
night

nine
ninety
no
nod
none
nope
nose
nosy
not
note
now
nude
numb
nut
nutty

O

o'clock
of
off
oil
okay
on
once
one
only
opposite
or
other
our
out
outside
oven
over

P

pace
pack
pad
page
paid
pain
pale
pan
pant
pants
park
part
party
pass
pat
patch
pay
payday
payment
pea
peck
peek
peel
peer
pen
penny
pep

pepper
pet
phone
pick
pie
pig
pile
pin
pine
Ping-Pong
pink
play
player
please
pod
poke
pole
pond
pop
Pope
pot
pretzel
problem
pump
punt
purse
put

Q

quack
queer
quick
quickly
quit
quite

R

race
rack
rage
rain
rake
ram
ramp
ran
rang
rank
rare
rat
rate
read
real
red
reel
refund
refuse
relax
remind
rent
rice
rid
ride
rig

right
ring
rip
ripe
road
rob
robber
robbery
robe
rock
rod
rode
role
room
rope
rose
rosy
rot
Roy
royal
rub
rude
rug
rule
ruler
run
rung
runt

S

sack
sad
sadly
safe
safely
said
sale
same
sand
sang
sank
sat
Saturday
save
saw
say
says
see
seed
seek
seem
seen
seep
send
sent
serve
set
she
should
shout
sick
side
sight

since
sing
singer
sink
sip
sit
six
sixty
sky
so
soak
soap
sob
sock
sole
some
something
song
soon
sorry
sort
start
stay
still
stop
street
sub
suds
Sue
sum
summer
sun
Sunday
sung
sunk
sunny
swung

T

tab
tack
take
tale
talk
tame
tan
tank
tap
tax
tea
temper
ten
tent
than
thank
that
that's
the
them
then
there
there's
they

thing
think
thinker
this
thought
thumb
Thursday
tick
tide
tie
tight
tile
Tim
tin
tire
to
today
Tom
tone
too
top
town
toy
track
true
try
tub
tube
Tuesday
tug
tune
turn

U

until
up
us
use

V

verse
very
voice
vote

W

wade
wage
wait
wake
walk
want
was
wasn't
water
wave
way
we
web
wed
Wednesday
weed
week
weekly

weep
well
went
were
wet
what
what's
when
where
which
while
who
why
wide
wife
wig
will
win
wine
wing
wink
winner
wipe
wire
wiry
witch
with
without
woke
woman
women
won
won't
wood
work
worker
would
wrap
wreck
wrist
write
writer
wrong
wrote

X

Y

year
yes
yesterday
yet
you
your
you're
yourself
Yule

Z

zip
zone
zoo

Lesson 13

The *r*-Controlled Vowel Combinations

air:	air	fair	hair	pair	stair
ear:	ear	dear	hear	near	year
ear:	bear	pear	tear	wear	swear
oar:	oar	roar	board		
oor:	door	doorway	poor	floor	
our:	our	hour	sour	flour	
our:	four	pour	court	course	

A Review of Sounds

car	dark	part	paid	mail	eat	clean	saw	now	cool
bar	bark	art	aid	fail	beat	bean	jaw	cow	fool
far	lark	cart	laid	jail	heat	jeans	law	how	pool
jar	mark	dart	maid	nail	neat	lean	paw	pow	tool
tar	park	smart	raid	tail	seat	mean	raw	wow	school

Words for Study

class	high	their	really
during	learn	picture	coffee
television	paint	worse	idea
evenings	teacher	forget	Joan

Night School

Dave had made up his mind to take a class at night school. He was getting tired of just going to work during the day. He was also tired of looking at television, hanging out with his friends, or seeing Linda in the evenings.

Dave had failed art in high school, but he still wanted to learn to paint. Maybe with the aid of a good teacher, he could pick up some hints on how to paint better.

On his first night, the teacher told them that their first class was going to be painting a picture of a pear. Dave worked for about an hour on his picture. He knew his picture didn't look like a pear at all. It looked more like a jar. He put a dab of paint here and a dab of paint there, but this only made his picture look worse.

Dave felt like a fool. He wanted to tear the picture up and forget all about night school.

Then a lovely woman, who was painting near Dave, said, "Wow, that really looks like a pear! How did you learn to paint like that?" Dave saw that the pear in her picture looked like a box.

Dave lied, "I have been painting for years. Your picture is good, too. Would you like to go to the diner down the street with me when we are done? I would like to buy you a cup of coffee. We can talk about painting."

"What a good idea!" the woman said. "I would love to. By the way, my name is Joan. What's your name?"

"Dave," said Dave. He wanted to look cool, so he went back to painting his pear. His painting didn't look so bad to him now. Night school was going to be a lot more fun than he thought it would be.

1 **Read and Write.** Use a word from the box for each sentence in the set.

| soon |
| moon |
| noon |

1. Do you know the verse which has this line: The cow jumped over the _____.

2. Bob said that he would meet Eddie at _____.

3. It would _____ be time for Kate to take the cake out of the oven.

| maid |
| mail |
| main |

4. Sue hoped there was a birthday card from her mom and dad in the _____.

5. The _____ act at the zoo was a bear and her four cubs.

6. Bob hired a _____ to come in once a week to clean his house.

| card |
| cart |
| carve |

7. Andy needed a better knife to _____ the beef.

8. When Aunt Louise bumped into the _____ in the parking lot, she hurt her arm.

9. Kate could not make up her mind which _____ she wanted to buy for Eddie.

| meat |
| meal |
| mean |

10. Tom fed his pet raw _____ for dinner.

11. Mr. and Mrs. Jones eat their main _____ at six o'clock.

12. The little girl was so _____ that she didn't have any friends.

| code |
| cone |
| cope |

13. Joan wrote the zip _____ on the card she sent her dad.

14. When Bob can't _____ with all the work, he gets a friend to help him.

15. Linda picked up a pine _____ at the park and put it in her purse.

| more |
| sore |
| tore |
| wore |

16. Dave _____ up his picture as soon as he got home.

17. Aunt Louise's arm was so _____ that she could not go to work for a week.

18. Mike _____ his new pants to the party Friday night.

19. Kids are _____ than happy when school is out for the summer.

lead	20. Linda didn't know that her gas tank had a _____ in it.
lean	21. Eddie liked _____ meat better than meat with a lot of fat in it.
leaf	22. The _____ singer in the band called in sick Tuesday night.
leak	23. Bucky knew it was time to turn over a new _____.

horn	24. Bob was _____ out from working so hard.
corn	25. Eddie honked the _____ four times, but Kate said that she didn't hear it.
born	26. Jack fixed ham and _____ for his evening meal.
torn	27. The rug was so _____ up from the cat's paws that Ben had to buy a new one.
worn	28. The baby was _____ at one o'clock in the morning.

2 **Read and Write.** More work with the ending -er.

boarder
catcher
diner
helper
keeper
painter
teacher
voter

_____ 1. Who would like the art classes at night school?

_____ 2. Who takes care of the monkeys at the zoo?

_____ 3. Who uses a mitt?

_____ 4. Who lives in your home and pays you for rent and food?

_____ 5. Who picks the men and women who want to run your town?

_____ 6. Who likes to go out to eat a lot?

_____ 7. Who gave you aid when you had a problem?

_____ 8. Who hopes you like doing this page of work?

3 **Word Study.** Pick the word that does not fit with the rest and write it on the line .

1. ear   head   lip   nose   _head_

2. evening   morning   noon   year   _____

3. beets   corn   pear   peas   _____

4. ace   dice   king   joker   _____

5. bake   boil   cook   oven   _____

6. air   beer   tea   water   _____

7. candy   food   gum   mints   _____

8. can   jar   jug   tea   _____

9. fake   real   right   true   _____

10. dues   fee   taxes   wages   _____

4 **Read and Write.** Mark the vowels.

1. ădd   5. send   9. fume   13. doze

2. bītę   6. clock   10. reel   14. dunk

3. gate   7. pop   11. hike   15. zone

4. damp   8. same   12. hunt   16. deck

58   Lesson 13

Lesson 14

Vowels Followed by the Letter /

al:	all	ball	bald	call	hall	fall	false	salt
el:	bell	belt	melt	held	help	tell	yell	self
il:	ill	bill	hill	fill	film	milk	spill	
ild:	mild	wild	child					
ol:	old	cold	gold	told	bolt	roll		
ul:	dull	bulb	pulse					
ull:	full	pull	bull					

Words for Study

give	stories	hi	mistake
open	however	eye	computer
minute	most	according	deal
must	almost	month	least

Paying Bills

Eddie stopped by Jack's house on his way home from work. He wanted to give Jack some film that he had picked up on sale downtown. It felt good to be doing something for Jack after all that Jack had done for him.

When Eddie opened the front door, he could hear Jack laughing loudly in the den. Eddie stayed in the hall for a minute. It was good to hear Jack laugh. "He must be reading that book Aunt Louise lent him," thought Eddie to himself. She had told Jack that he would get a big kick out of the writer's funny stories.

However, when Eddie walked into the den, he saw that Jack wasn't reading the book. In fact, he was doing what he hated the most. Jack was paying his bills.

Now, Jack was a mild man who almost never lost his temper. However, bills and taxes always seemed to turn Jack into a wild man. All of Jack's friends knew that when he was paying his bills, he would swear a little, yell a lot, and just about pull his hair out. At the rate Jack was going, he was lucky that he wasn't bald yet.

"Jack," said Eddie, "you're not ill, are you?"

"Hi, Eddie," laughed Jack. "It's good to see you. Have a seat." Jack was laughing so hard that his eyes were filled with tears.

"Are you going to tell me what's so funny?" asked Eddie.

Jack handed Eddie his phone bill. When Eddie saw it, he started laughing, too. According to the bill, Jack's payment for the month was only ten cents. "Wow, what a mistake!" said Eddie. "The computer really gave you a good deal this month. What are you going to do?"

"Why, I'm going to send them a dime, of course," laughed Jack. "Paying bills is so dull and boring that I might as well have a little fun this time. How do you feel about paying bills?"

Eddie thought for a minute and then said, "Well, I'm so happy that I have a job that I don't mind paying bills right now. It feels good to have the money to pay them."

"That's not a bad idea," said Jack. "Maybe I should try to look at paying bills that way, too."

"You should," laughed Eddie. "At least it might keep you from going bald."

1 **Read and Write.** Add -*ful* to the words and then put them on the right lines.

hand + ful = _handful_

harm + ful = _____

help + ful = _____

care + ful = _____

use + ful = _____

thank + ful = _____

1. Bob told Dan that some of the tools were so old that they were no longer _____.

2. Kate gave Mary a _handful_ of pennies to buy some gum with.

3. After Jack had helped Aunt Louise start her car, she thanked him for being so _____.

4. Do you think that _____ thoughts can hurt others?

5. When Sue saw the child climbing up the pole, she told him to be _____.

6. Aunt Louise felt _____ that her life was so happy.

2 **Read and Write.** Add -*less* to the words and then put them on the right lines.

harm + less = _harmless_

help + less = _____

hope + less = _____

home + less = _____

care + less = _____

job + less = _____

1. Eddie was _____ for four months.

2. The little girl was sent to her room for being _____ with matches.

3. The fire on Main Street left five men and women _____.

4. The man waiting in the lobby looked very mean, but he was really _harmless_.

5. Ben tried for an hour to find his missing pet and then said, "It's _____."

6. Some men think that women are quite _____ when it comes to taking care of cars.

3 **Read and Write.** Match the words that mean the same thing.

handy

shout

dead   _____   1. cut

hurt   _____   2. sick

soaked

film   _____   3. useful

poor   _____   4. movie

ill   _____   5. all wet

carve   _____   6. yell

bare
              _____   7. harm

              _____   8. nude

              _____   9. needy

              _____   10. not living

4 **Read and Write.** Match the words that are opposite in meaning.

day   _____   1. hot

messy

take   _____   2. stop

harmless   _____   3. night

start

cold   _____   4. better

others   _____   5. give

false

worse   _____   6. neat

dumb
              _____   7. self

              _____   8. true

              _____   9. smart

              _____   10. harmful

5 **Sayings.** Put the words at the left on the right lines.

ball
bell
call
cold
fall
fill
hills
milk
✓ told
will

1. What you can say when your friend makes a mistake that you knew

   he would make:

   I hate to say it, but I ___*told*___ you so.

2. What you can say to your friends if you think they might need you:

   If you need any help, just give me a _____ .

3. What your mom used to tell you when you went outside to play:

   Put on your coat so you don't catch a _____ .

4. What you can say when you forget names:

   Their names don't ring a _____ .

5. What you can say to a friend who feels bad about a mistake:

   Don't cry over spilled _____ .

6. What you can say when you hear a bad joke:

   That joke is as old as the _____ .

7. What Mary says about Bob when he has a very good day at work:

   Bob is really on the _____ .

8. What you can say when you set a goal for yourself:

   Where there's a _____ , there's a way.

9. What you can say when men and women at the top make bad mistakes:

   The bigger they are, the harder they _____ .

10. What you can say when you need gas and have lots of money with you:

   _____ it up!

Lesson 15

Digraphs and Consonant Blends

ch			**sh**		
chase	cheap	chin	shake	share	shine
chair	chest	choose	shop	shock	short
teach	march	rich	cash	fish	rush
reach	church	lunch	dash	wish	hush

st			**sk**		
stand	step	still	skate	skin	skill
stop	store	stuff	skirt	skunk	sky
waste	west	east	ask	task	desk
last	toast	burst	mask	risk	dusk

Words for Study

couldn't	nobody	boss	anything
heard	two	I'll	those
drop	holding	toward	million
people	pointed	manager	fainted

Kate Saves the Day

It was Saturday morning, and Eddie and Kate were looking for something to do. "Why don't we go downtown," said Kate. "I want to buy a new chair for my room. You can help me pick it out."

Eddie hated shopping, but he couldn't think of a better idea, so they got into the car and went to the store at the end of West Street. Kate wished she were rich so she could choose any chair she wanted, but she knew she would end up buying something cheap.

There were four or five people in the store when they got there. It was so still in the store that you could hear a pin drop. "Why aren't people talking?" Kate asked Eddie in a hushed voice.

Then they saw why nobody was talking. Two short men wearing masks were holding up the store.

"Reach for the sky, you two," shouted one of the masked men who pointed a gun at Eddie's chest.

Kate got mad. "You can't boss us around like that," she shouted back. "I'll teach you a thing or two if it's the last thing I do."

The robbers were so shocked by the tone of Kate's voice that they lost all their nerve. As she marched toward them, the two men dashed out of the store as if they were being chased by real cops.

The people in the store were very thankful. The manager said she could have anything in the store that she wanted. Everybody was happy but Eddie.

"You are a real fool," said Eddie to Kate. "What if one of those jerks had fired at you? Then where would you be?"

"Well, they didn't, and they couldn't have fired if they wanted to," said Kate as she walked over to where one of the robbers had dropped his gun. "See, it's just a toy," said Kate as she picked up the gun and fired it at a lamp near the front door.

The lamp burst into a million bits. "Eddie," Kate cried, "this is a real gun!" Kate fainted on the spot.

1 **Read and Write.** Add *-est* to these words.

1. near + est = _nearest_

2. cheap + est = _____

3. rich + est = _____

4. smart + est = _____

5. loud + est = _____

1. fine + est = _finest_

2. safe + est = _____

3. rude + est = _____

4. ripe + est = _____

5. late + est = _____

1. big + est = _biggest_

2. hot + est = _____

3. fat + est = _____

4. mad + est = _____

5. red + est = _____

2 **Read and Write.** Change the *y* to *i* and add *-est*.

funny + est = *funniest*

happy + est = _____

lucky + est = _____

fussy + est = _____

lovely + est = _____

1. To some people, it seems that women look _____ when they are in love.

2. Mrs. West's child always acted the _____ when she put him down for his nap.

3. Of all his friends, Eddie thought Bob was the _____ because he had gotten his job first.

4. When Dave told Linda he would take her out for dinner, she felt like the _____ woman in town.

5. Andy was the *funniest* man at the party.

3 **Read and Write.** Choose the right word and write it on the line.

chest *or* chess

1. Dave didn't know how people could stand to play

   _____.

add *or* odd

2. To him, it seemed _____ that they could be happy playing this game hour after hour.

share *or* sharp

3. Dave knew that chess players had to have _____ minds to win the game.

talked *or* tall

4. Dave thought you could have just as sharp a mind if you

   _____ with friends.

walk *or* wall

5. Linda loved to play chess. When Dave tried to tell her

   how he felt about the game, it was like talking to a _____.

load, loan, *or* loaf

6. When Linda played chess with Mike on Wednesday

   nights, Dave would _____ around the house.

base, case, *or* vase

7. Just in _____ Linda would think he was wasting his time, Dave would have a book in front of him.

wrote, vote, *or* quote

8. If it were up to Dave, he would _____ to put an end to all chess games.

last, fast, *or* past

9. _____ week, Mike beat Linda, and she was in a bad mood when she met Dave for coffee at the diner.

well, fell, *or* sell

10. Dave hoped she would play _____ next Wednesday because he didn't like putting up with her bad moods.

4 **Read and Write.** Match the words that mean the same thing.

boring
chair   _____   1. hope for
drop   _____   2. let go of
faint   _____   3. ripped
queer
torn   _____   4. pull
tug   _____   5. odd
two
wish   _____   6. pass out
must   _____   7. seat

_____   8. dull

_____   9. pair

_____   10. have to

Lesson 16

Consonant Blends

bl:	blame	black	bleed	bless	blind	block
cl:	clear	clip	close	clothes	cloth	club
fl:	flame	flat	flock	flour	flush	fly
gl:	glass	glad	gland	glare	gleam	glue
pl:	place	plate	plane	plan	plug	plus
sl:	slam	sleep	sleeve	slice	slip	slow

Words for Study

such	nurse	many	rest
badly	goodness	ever	death
Dr.	does	surprised	before
spite	heart	haven't	often

Love

Bob was in such a rush to get to work Friday morning that he slammed his hand in the car door. Almost at once, his hand started to turn black and blue. He picked up an old cloth that was on the floor of his car and wrapped it quickly around his hand. He saw that his thumb was cut. It was bleeding so badly that the cloth was soon red. Bob felt as if he were going to faint.

It was Bob's luck that Dr. Chase's place was in the middle of the next block. In spite of the pain, Bob ran as fast as he could to Dr. Chase's. When he got there, he saw a lovely nurse sitting behind the desk. When she saw Bob's hand, she cried, "My goodness! Does it hurt very much?"

But, by now, Bob wasn't thinking about his hand. He was looking at the nurse, and his heart was beating very fast. The nurse was June Baker. Bob had dated her many years ago when they were in high school. She had been his first true love. Bob had not seen June for six years. She was still the loveliest girl he had ever known.

Then June looked from Bob's hand, which was bleeding all over the rug, to his face. "Why, Bob!" she said in a very surprised voice. "I haven't seen you in ages! Your hand looks bad, but the rest of you looks just fine," she laughed. "It's really good to see you again."

"It's good to see you, too," Bob said. "How about going out with me Saturday night? We can talk about the good old days, and what we are doing now."

"I would love to," said June. "But now, let me get your hand fixed up, so you don't bleed to death before our date."

Bob felt so happy that he thought he would really faint now. As Aunt Louise was always saying, "Bad times can turn into good times a lot more often than people think."

Bob was in all this pain and late for work; yet he had not felt this good for a long, long time.

1 Read and Write. Put the words in the boxes on the right lines.

| house |
| mouse |
| blouse |

1. If you saw a _____ in your _____, what would you do?

2. Kate wore a red _____ and a black skirt to work yesterday.

| toast |
| roast |
| coast |

3. Cape Cod is on the East _____.

4. Do you ever put jam on your _____?

5. Dave was so fond of _____ beef that he ate it at least once a week.

| new |
| flew |
| blew |

6. The plane _____ to the West Coast in less than four hours.

7. "Is that a _____ blouse you're wearing?" asked Kate's boss.

8. The man _____ out the match just before it burned his thumb.

| pale |
| tales |
| stale |

9. Do nurses turn _____ when they see people bleeding?

10. The pretzels were so _____ that Ben fed them to his cat.

11. Aunt Louise had many funny _____ to tell about the days when she worked in a coffee shop.

dip
slip
ship

12. "Be careful that you don't _____ on the floor," said Jack. "I just mopped it."

13. Bob was so hot after working all day that he took a quick

_____ in his boss's pool before he went home.

14. Dan told the man to _____ the new tools as soon as he could.

reach
beach
bleached
each

15. There were just enough pretzels so that _____ child could have six.

16. Eddie tried for an hour to _____ Kate on the phone.

17. Sue _____ the jeans that she planned to wear to the

_____ on Sunday.

page
rage
stage

18. Mark flew into a _____ when he couldn't find his socks.

19. Ever since Sue had the leading role in a high school play, she

wanted to be on the _____.

20. From the very first _____, Jack knew that the book was going to amuse him.

pain
plain
stains

21. It was _____ to June that Bob was in a lot of _____.

22. Kate came back from lunch with ketchup _____ all over her new blouse.

same
shame
lame
blamed

23. Linda thought it was a _____ that Mark was _____.

24. Joan left her things around the house so often that she never

_____ other people when they did the _____ thing.

rush
slush
blush

25. The roads were really bad at _____ hour because the

_____ slowed the driving to ten miles an hour.

26. Do you _____ when people tell you something nice about yourself?

| matter |
| platter |
| shattered |

27. When Joan dropped the _____, and it _____ all over the floor, she said, "There's one less dish to clean."

28. "What's the _____?" asked Dave. "You look pale."

| nap |
| map |
| slap |
| clapped |

29. Ms. Bond looked at the _____ to see how many miles she still had to go.

30. The people in the stands _____ for two minutes when the catcher hit a home run.

31. Just before Kate lay down for her Sunday _____, she told Aunt Louise to _____ her a few times at four o'clock so she would not miss the game on television.

2 Read and Write. Use a word from A, add a word from B to it, and fill in the lines.

A	B
base	ball
cook	ball
cup	boat
✓down	book
foot	cakes
home	end
house	hold
life	✓town
sun	shine
week	work

1. Eddie and Kate went _downtown_ Saturday night to see a movie.

2. People like to play _____ in the summer.

3. People like to play _____ in the fall.

4. Mary asked Aunt Louise if she would teach her how to bake _____ .

5. Kate used a _____ when she baked cakes and pies.

6. When they knew the ship was going down, each man, woman, and child climbed quickly into the _____.

7. Saturday and Sunday are called the _____.

8. After Mary did all her _____, her dad said she could go outside and play for an hour.

9. When Mr. and Mrs. Hope were asked who was the head of their _____, they pointed to each other at the same time.

10. No matter how bad things got, Aunt Louise was always willing to put a little _____ into other people's lives.

3 Read and Write.

1. After a fight, do you shake hands and make up, or do you go home in a bad mood?

_____

2. Which do you like better, baseball or football?

_____

3. Do you think your writing is neat, or is it hard to read?

_____

4. Do you like beef rare, or do you cook it until it is well-done?

_____

5. Do you go to church on Sunday, or do you sleep late that morning?

_____

Word Index: Lessons 1-16

A
a
about
according
ace
act
add
after
again
age
ago
aid
ail
air
all
all right
almost
alone
also
always
am
amuse
amusement
an
and
Andy
ant
any
anything
are
aren't
around
arm
art
as
ask
at
ate
aunt
awake
awoke

B
baby
back
bad
badly
bake
baker
bald
ball
band
bang

bank
banker
bar
bare
bark
barn
base
baseball
bat
batch
be
beach
bean
bear
beat
because
bed
beef
been
beep
beer
beet
before
behind
bell
belt
Ben
bend
bent
bet
better
bib
big
bike
bill
bind
birth
birthday
bit
bite
black
blame
bleach
bleed
bless
blew
blind
block
blouse
blue
blush
board

boarder
boat
Bob
boil
bolt
bomb
bond
bone
bony
book
bore
born
boss
box
boxer
boy
buck
Bucky
bud
bug
bulb
bull
bum
bump
bumper
bumpy
bun
bunk
bunt
burn
burner
burp
burst
bus
but
buy
by

C
cab
cage
cake
call
came
can
candy
cane
can't
cap
cape
Cape Cod
car
card

care
careful
careless
cart
carve
case
cash
cat
catch
catcher
celebrate
cent
chair
chase
cheap
chess
chest
child
chin
choose
church
clap
class
clean
clear
climb
clip
clock
close
cloth
clothes
club
coal
coast
coat
cod
code
coffee
Coke
cold
come
computer
cone
cook
cookbook
cool
cop
cope
copper
corn
cot
could

couldn't
count
course
court
cow
cry
cub
cube
cup
cupcake
curve
cut
cute

D
dab
dad
daddy
dam
damp
Dan
dare
dark
dart
dash
date
Dave
day
dead
deal
dear
death
deck
deer
den
dent
desk
dice
Dick
did
didn't
die
dig
dime
dine
diner
dinner
dip
dirt
dish
ditch
dive
do

dock
does
done
donkey
don't
door
doorway
dope
dot
down
downtown
doze
Dr.
drop
duck
due
dues
dug
duke
dull
dumb
dump
dune
dunk
during
dusk
Dutch

E
each
ear
east
eat
Eddie
eel
end
ending
enough
evening
ever
eye

F
face
fact
fad
fade
fail
faint
fair
fake
fall
false

fame
fang
far
fare
fast
fat
fed
fee
feed
feel
feet
fell
felt
female
fetch
few
fig
fight
fighter
file
fill
film
find
fine
fire
firm
firmly
first
fish
fit
five
fix
flame
flat
flew
flock
floor
flour
flush
fly
fond
food
fool
foot
football
for
forget
fork
forty
four
fox
Friday

friend
friendly
from
front
full
fume
fun
fund(s)
funk
funny
fuse
fuss
fussy

G

game
gas
gate
gave
get
girl
girlfriend
give
glad
gland
glare
glass
gleam
glue
go
goal
God
gold
gone
gong
good
goodness
got
gotten
gum
gun
guy

H

had
hair
hall
ham
hammer
hand
handful
handy
hang
happy
hard
harm

harmful
harmless
hat
hate
have
haven't
he
head
hear
heard
heart
heat
heck
heel
held
help
helper
helpful
helpless
hen
her
herd
here
herself
hi
hid
hide
hide-and-seek
high
high school
hike
hill
him
himself
hint
hip
hire
his
hit
hitter
hock
hold
hole
home
homeless
home run
homework
honk
hop
hope
hopeless
horn
horse
hose
hot

hour
house
household
how
however
hug
huge
hum
hung
hunt
hunter
hurt
hush
hut

I

I
ice
icy
idea
if
ill
I'll
I'm
in
ink
into
is
it
itch
it's

J

jab
Jack
jack
jail
jam
jar
jaw
jazz
jeans
jeep
jerk
Joan
job
jobless
join
joint
joke
joker
Jones
jot
joy
jug
jump

June
junk
just

K

Kate
keel
keep
keeper
ketchup
key
kick
kid
kind
king
kiss
kit
kite
knee
knew
knife
knock
know
known

L

lab
lace
lack
lacy
laid
lake
lamb
lame
lamp
land
lane
lap
lark
last
late
later
laugh
law
lay
lead
leaf
leak
lean
learn
least
led
left
lend
lent
less
let

let's
lick
lid
lie
life
lifeboat
light
like
lime
limp
Linda
line
lint
lip
little
live
living
load
loaf
loan
lobby
lock
lone
long
look
lord
lose
lost
lot(s)
loud
loudly
Louise
love
lovely
loyal
luck
lucky
lug
lump
lunch
lung

M

Mack
mad
made
maid
mail
main
make
male
man
manager
many
map
march

mark
Mary
mask
mat
match
mate
matter
may
maybe
me
meal
mean
meat
meet
meeting
melt
men
mend
mess
messy
met
mice
middle
might
Mike
mile
mild
milk
million
mind
mine
mint
minute
miss
mistake
mitt
mix
mob
mock
mom
mommy
Monday
money
monkey
month
mood
moon
mop
more
morning
most
mouse
movie
Mr.
Mrs.

Ms.
much
mud
muddy
mug
mugger
mule
muse
must
mute
my
myself

N

nail
name
nap
near
neat
neck
need
needy
nerve
net
never
new
next
nice
nick
night
nine
ninety
no
nobody
nod
none
noon
nope
nose
nosy
not
note
now
nude
numb
nurse
nut
nutty

O

oar
o'clock
odd
of
off
often

oil
okay
old
on
once
one
only
open
opposite
or
other
our
out
outside
oven
over

P

pace
pack
pad
page
paid
pain
paint
painter
painting
pair
pale
pan
pant
pants
park
part
party
pass
past
pat
patch
paw
pay
payday
payment
pea
pear
peck
peek
peel
peer
pen
penny
people
pep
pepper
pet
phone

pick
picture
pie
pig
pile
pin
pine
Ping-Pong
pink
place
plain
plan
plane
plate
platter
play
player
please
plug
plus
pod
point
poke
pole
pond
pool
poor
pop
Pope
pot
pour
pretzel
problem
pull
pulse
pump
punt
purse
put

Q

quack
queer
quick
quickly
quit
quite
quote

R

race
rack
rage
raid
rain
rake
ram

ramp
ran
rang
rank
rare
rat
rate
raw
reach
read
real
really
red
reel
refund
refuse
relax
remind
rent
rest
rice
rich
rid
ride
rig
right
ring
rip
ripe
risk
road
roar
roast
rob
robber
robbery
robe
rock
rod
rode
role
roll
room
rope
rose
rosy
rot
Roy
royal
rub
rude
rug
rule
ruler
run

rung
runt
rush

S

sack
sad
sadly
safe
safely
said
sale
salt
same
sand
sang
sank
sat
Saturday
save
saw
say
saying
says
school
seat
see
seed
seek
seem
seen
seep
self
sell
send
sent
serve
set
shake
shame
share
sharp
shatter
she
shine
ship
shock
shop
short
should
shout
sick
side
sight
since
sing

singer
sink
sip
sit
six
sixty
skate
skill
skin
skirt
skunk
sky
slam
slap
sleep
sleeve
slice
slip
slow
slush
smart
so
soak
soap
sob
sock
sole
some
something
song
soon
sore
sorry
sort
sour
spill
spite
stage
stain
stair
stale
stand
start
stay
step
still
stop
store
story
street
stuff
sub
such
suds
Sue

sum
summer
sun
Sunday
sung
sunk
sunny
sunshine
surprise
swear
swung

T

tab
tack
tail
take
tale
talk
tall
tame
tan
tank
tap
tar
task
tax
tea
teach
teacher
tear
television
tell
temper
ten
tent
than
thank
thankful
that
that's
the
their
them
then
there
there's
they
thing
think
thinker
this
those
thought
thumb
Thursday

tick
tide
tie
tight
tile
Tim
time
tin
tire
to
toast
today
told
Tom
tone
too
took
tool
top
tore
torn
toward
town
toy
track
true
try
tub
tube
Tuesday
tug
tune
turn
two

U

until
up
us
use
useful

V

vase
verse
very
voice
vote
voter

W

wade
wage
wait
wake
walk
wall

want
was
wasn't
waste
water
wave
way
we
wear
web
wed
Wednesday
weed
week
weekend
weekly
weep
well
well-done
went
were
west
wet
what
what's
when
where
which
while
who
why
wide
wife
wig
wild
will
win
wine
wing
wink
winner
wipe
wire
wiry
wish
witch
with
without
woke
woman
women
won
won't
wood
word

wore
work
worker
worn
worse
would
wow
wrap
wreck
wrist
write
writer
writing
wrong
wrote

X

Y

year
yell
yes
yesterday
yet
you
your
you're
yourself
Yule

Z

zip
zone
zoo

Lesson 17

More Consonant Blends

br:	brave	brain	bread	bride	broke	brown
cr:	crazy	crash	cream	crime	crown	crumb
dr:	drain	dream	dress	drive	drove	dry
fr:	freeze	free	fresh	French	froze	fry
gr:	grape	gray	grass	green	groom	ground
pr:	pray	pride	prize	print	proud	prune
tr:	tray	train	trail	tree	treat	trip
str:	straw	stream	strike	string	stroke	strong

Words for Study

even	decide	hadn't	calm
both	shirt	whole	ready
upset	slacks	jacket	anywhere
able	steak	cleaner	check

Bob Has a Problem

It was Saturday morning, and Bob thought the night would never come. Running into June at Dr. Chase's was like a dream come true. Bob was so happy that he didn't even mind the fact that his hand still hurt. He didn't even mind that Dan Rose had yelled at him for five minutes on the phone because Bob wasn't strong enough to go back to work yet.

Both Dan and Bob knew it would be crazy for Bob to work on bikes with his hand all wrapped up. Dan was just upset that his prize worker was out sick. Bob knew he would be able to go to work by the middle of next week.

Right now, all Bob wanted to think about was how he was going to dress for his date with June. He picked out a dark-green shirt and a pair of light-gray slacks. Bob was proud of his clothes. Even when he was at work, he took pride in how he looked.

Next, he had to decide where to take June. They could drive out to the Steak House and have a steak dinner with French fries and a glass of wine. And after that? Maybe they would see a movie or go for a walk in the park.

Bob told himself to slow down. The night hadn't even started yet, and he was trying to plan the whole evening without any idea of what June wanted to do.

He put on his jacket to go downtown and pick up his good coat from the dry cleaners. That would calm him down a bit. It would also make the time go faster.

He was just getting ready to step out the front door when he froze in his tracks. All his lovely dreams were going to go down the drain! Since Bob had missed work yesterday, he didn't get his check. How could he take June anywhere when he didn't have a dime to his name?

1 **Read and Write.** Put the words in the boxes on the right lines.

slow
blow
flow
row

1. When Dan heard that Bob would miss a few days of work, it came as quite a _____ to him.

2. Joan wished she could get the water to _____ a lot faster from her sink.

3. The boys were _____ in getting back to the dock because they had only one oar to _____ the boat with.

pride
prizes
price

4. "What was the _____ of those new tools?" asked Bob.

5. Mary was filled with _____ when she won two _____ for her work in art class.

tested
toast
taste

6. Jack fixed himself two slices of _____ for his lunch.

7. The slices didn't _____ hot enough, so he _____ the toaster to see what the problem was.

chest
best
pcsts
vests

8. When Dan asked Bob if he would be back to work by Tuesday, he said, "I'll try my _____."

9. Eddie's _____ was so big that none of the _____ he tried on fit him right.

10. Which household _____ do you think are worse—ants or flies?

brown
clown
gown

11. The _____ at the amusement park wore a woman's evening _____ with huge _____ dots all over it.

truck
trunk
trust

12. After Mr. Jones had filled the _____ of his car with junk, he still had some stuff he wanted to get rid of.

13. His wife said that she would rent a _____.

14. Mr. Jones said, "I don't know if I _____ you driving a truck all the way out to the dump by yourself. I know how you drive."

harming
charming
farm

15. Bob knew that he would just be _____ himself if he went back to work too soon.

16. Many people who live in big towns think that life on a

_____ must be very _____.

may
hay
prayed
clay

17. Mary made a lovely _____ pot in art class which she

thinks her mom _____ want to put in the living room.

18. The farmers _____ that all the _____ did not burn up in the fire last night.

drops
stopped
crops

19. When the first _____ of rain fell, Kate _____ reading her book and ran out to get the clothes that were hanging on the line.

20. The farmers didn't make as much money from their

_____ last summer as they thought they would.

gum
plums
drum

21. When Mary asked if she could buy some _____, her dad

said, "Why don't you eat one of those _____? That would be much better for you."

22. Mack hoped his friends would pool their money and buy him a

_____ set for his birthday.

2 **Read and Write.** Choose the words that have to do with a *town* and put them in the first row. Put the words that have to do with a *school* in the middle row. Put the words that have to do with a *farm* in the last row. (USE EACH WORD ONLY ONCE.)

✓ barn
bus stops
churches
classes
courses
cows
crops
hay
hens
homework
parks
reading
stores
street lights
teachers

Town	School	Farm
1. _____	1. _____	1. _barn_
2. _____	2. _____	2. _____
3. _____	3. _____	3. _____
4. _____	4. _____	4. _____
5. _____	5. _____	5. _____

3 **Read and Write.**

Which do you
like *best*?

Which do you
like *least*?

_____   1. fried fish, ham, roast beef, or steak   _____

_____   2. black, blue, green, or pink   _____

_____   3. baseball, football, Ping-Pong, or track   _____

_____   4. grapes, plums, pears, or prunes   _____

_____   5. cake, candy, ice cream, or pie   _____

_____   6. Monday, Friday, Saturday, or Sunday   _____

_____   7. buses, cabs, planes, or trains   _____

_____   8. beer, coffee, milk, or tea   _____

_____   9. bankers, boxers, singers, or teachers   _____

_____   10. movies, parks, television, or zoos   _____

Lesson 18

More Digraphs and Consonant Blends

wh:	whale	wheat	wheel	white	whip
th:	this	that	these	those	
	thick	thin	third	thirty	thirteen
	tooth	teeth	north	south	math
thr:	three	throw	threw	through	
tw:	twelve	twenty	twice	twin	twist
sm:	smash	small	smell	smile	smoke
sn:	snake	snail	sneeze	snore	snow
sp:	space	speak	spoon	spot	spank
sw:	sweet	sweat	swim	swift	switch

Words for Study

mother	afternoon	worst	everybody
father	cousin	legs	calmly
watch	grade	number	I've
Billy	sure	show	nothing

A Way with Kids

Mary's mother and father asked Jack if he would watch Billy that Saturday afternoon. They wanted to take Mary to a play. Billy was Mary's cousin. He was staying with them for a few weeks. He was six years old and was in the first grade.

As the three were going out the door, Mary's mother said, "Thank you so much for helping us out, Jack. Just be firm with Billy, and I'm sure that things will be all right."

Well, it started out to be one of the worst afternoons of Jack's life. He had no sooner closed the front door when Billy smashed him in the chest with a toy. Just as Jack was thinking that Billy might need a good spanking, Billy wheeled his bike into the room and rolled it right into Jack's legs.

Jack let out a yell because he had twisted his knee yesterday, and his whole leg was sore. He was about to swear, but then he thought, "If I lose my temper, things will get worse. Maybe if I speak to him in the right way, things will get better."

"Billy," said Jack. "Have you learned about numbers in math yet?"

Billy said, "Sure, I know all about numbers."

"Good," said Jack. "Now, tell me this. Which number is bigger—six or three?"

"Six," laughed Billy. "Everybody knows that!"

"Right. You are a smart boy," smiled Jack. "Now I'm over six feet tall, and you're maybe three feet tall. What do you think that means?"

Billy may have been a little wild, but he was no fool. He knew just what Jack was talking about.

When Mary and her father and mother came home at three-thirty, Billy was sitting calmly on the floor and playing with his toy trucks. Jack was watching a movie on television.

"My goodness!" said Mary's mother. "You sure do have a way with kids. I've never seen Billy this calm."

"It's nothing," Jack smiled. "You just have to know how to talk to them, that's all."

1 **Read and Write.** Put the words in the boxes on the right lines.

left
lift

1. Dave was able to give Linda a _____ to work on Tuesday.

2. The skunk _____ a smell that lasted for hours.

gift
shift

3. Mary's mother gave Jack a _____ for being so kind.

4. Dave hoped he would be switched from the third to the first _____ at the shop where he worked.

math
bath
path

5. Mary wanted to see the show on television, so she tried to do her _____ homework while she was taking a _____ .

6. If Bucky had been able to find the _____ , he could have climbed to the top of the hill in less than twenty minutes.

hill
chill
spilled
grilled

7. It took Bucky over an hour to climb to the top of the _____ .

8. Mary _____ her ice cream cone all over her jacket.

9. Do you like meat better when it's baked or _____ ?

10. Aunt Louise had to _____ the pie, so it wouldn't taste stale the next day.

dare
fare
flares
spare

11. "Don't you _____ walk on this floor," said Eddie. "I just got through mopping it."

12. Ms. Bond didn't have enough money for cab _____ , so she took the bus to work.

13. Aunt Louise really wanted to lend her cousin the money, but she couldn't _____ the cash.

14. The men lit _____ so other drivers would see the wreck.

lit
pit
spit

15. The baseball player _____ on the ball.

16. The fox fell into the _____ that the hunters had dug to catch him.

17. Andy _____ a match so he could see where the light switch was.

bib
fibs
ribs
crib

18. Did you ever tell your mother or father _____ when you were a child?

19. The mother took off the baby's _____ and put him in the _____ for his afternoon nap.

20. The man was so thin from not eating right that you could see his _____.

coast
coals
coach

21. The _____ let the players rest for twenty minutes.

22. Jack checked to see if the _____ was clear before he hid the gift in the den.

23. Eddie let the _____ die down before he put the spare-ribs on the grill.

2 Numbers. Read these number words.

one (1)	six (6)	eleven (11)	sixteen (16)
two (2)	seven (7)	twelve (12)	seventeen (17)
three (3)	eight (8)	thirteen (13)	eighteen (18)
four (4)	nine (9)	fourteen (14)	nineteen (19)
five (5)	ten (10)	fifteen (15)	twenty (20)

Write the word for the right sum on each line.

1. eleven plus seven _____

2. nineteen plus one _____

3. twelve plus three _____

4. eight plus seven _____

5. eight plus eight _____

6. seven plus four _____

7. thirteen plus two _____

8. five plus two _____

9. two plus two _____

10. twelve plus one _____

Write the right number word on each line.

_____ 11. How many days are in a week?

_____ 12. How many months are in a year?

_____ 13. How many meals do you eat each day?

_____ 14. How many tires does a car have?

_____ 15. What is your lucky number?

_____ 16. How many cousins do you have?

_____ 17. How many hours do you sleep each night?

_____ 18. How old were you when you first drove a car?

_____ 19. How many times have you fainted in your life?

_____ 20. According to an old saying, how many lives does a cat have?

3 **Read and Write.** Use a word from **A**, add a word from **B** to it, and fill in the lines.

A	B
✓arm	book
bath	book
bed	burn
check	cakes
down	✓chair
note	corn
pan	room
pop	room
short	stairs
sun	stop

1. Dan turned on the lamp next to his _armchair_ so he could see what he was reading.

2. Sue stayed at the beach too long and got a mild _____.

3. "While you're in the _____," shouted Kate to Aunt Louise, "will you check the water in the tub?"

4. "Don't forget your math _____ on Monday," the teacher said.

5. Eddie got two boxes of _____ in the lobby before the movie started.

6. Dave had twin beds in his _____.

7. Joan was glad that she didn't have her _____ with her because she wanted to buy all the clothes in the store.

8. The manager told the _____ to lay a bunt down the first base line.

9. Most people eat _____ in the morning, but Sue liked to serve them for dinner now and then.

10. Jack went _____ to check the meat in the oven.

Lesson 19

Still More Consonant Blends

sc:	scare	scar	scarf	score	scout
scr:	scratch	screen	screech	scream	scrub
shr:	shrimp	shrink	shrank	shrunk	shrug
spl:	splash	spleen	split	splint	splinter
spr:	spray	sprain	sprawl	sprint	spring
squ:	square	squeeze	squeak	squeal	squirrel
str:	stream	stretch	strike	strong	strip
chr:	chrome	Christ	Christmas	Christian	

Words for Study

sound	steering	body	anyway
police	another	across	we're
crowd	yards	else	star
between	blood	hey	beside

How Kate Got to Be a Movie Star

Kate was scrubbing the floor when she heard the sound of screeching tires in front of her house. She looked out the screen door just in time to see a car strike a tree. Screams came from the car. Kate rushed to the phone and called the police. Then she dashed outside to see if she could help. There was a small crowd around the smashed car.

Kate thought she would faint. She couldn't tell if the people in the car were living or dead. The driver was squeezed between the front seat and the steering wheel. Another man was sprawled on the ground about ten yards from the car. Blood was streaming down his left arm. A third body was stretched out across the back seat of the car.

Kate was getting more and more upset. The people in the crowd were talking and taking notes. Nobody was even trying to help the three men. Also, no police had come yet. What was wrong with this crowd? Didn't these people even care? Kate wished that Aunt Louise were home. She would know what to do. However, Aunt Louise was not home, and this was no time to be scared. Even if nobody else cared about these poor men, at least Kate did.

She sprinted across the street to help the man who lay sprawled on the ground. She was running so fast that she tripped over some strips of chrome that were all over the ground. She fell right on top of the man she was trying to help. The man on the ground gave her a very surprised look. Kate's arms and legs were scratched up from her fall. She was bleeding all over the man on the ground.

Then a man wearing a gold scarf around his neck screamed at Kate. "Hey, you. What do you think you're doing anyway? Can't you see we're making a movie? Get out of here. You're messing up the film." Kate's face turned red. In fact, it turned redder than the fake blood on the movie star who was sprawled on the ground beside her.

1 **Read and Write.** Choose the right word and write it on the line.

wrist, list, *or* fist

1. Ms. Bond was making out her Christmas shopping
   _____ .

shops, chops, *or* flops

2. Since her friends thought her gifts were _____ ,
   she didn't like Christmas shopping at all.

boss, loss, *or* cross

3. Last year, she sent her _____ a cap she had knitted
   that was too small.

bath, math, *or* path

4. She had wrapped a number book for Mary to help
   her with her _____ . Mary thought it was a dumb
   gift.

leg, beg, *or* egg

5. She had painted an _____ for Kate to hang on the
   Christmas tree, but it looked so messy that Kate hung
   it in the back of the tree.

mother, brother, *or* other

6. The _____ people on Ms. Bond's Christmas
   list were just as upset with their gifts.

spilled *or* thrilled

7. As Ms. Bond thought about last Christmas, she got
   so upset that she _____ her tea all over the
   floor.

fork, pork, *or* stork

8. As she cleaned up the mess, a _____ next to the
   sink fell and hit her on the head.

wipe, stripe, *or* swipe

9. She was mad now, so she didn't _____ up the
   rest of the mess.

threw, chew, *or* drew

10. In fact, she was so mad that she tore up her list and
    _____ it up in the air.

steam, team, *or* cream

11. As she got out the _____ for another cup of
    tea, she had a funny thought.

snow, bow, *or* low

12. Maybe it would _____ so badly this year that
    Christmas shopping would be called off.

2 **Read and Write.** Fill in the line with the right word from the row at the left.

black
blue
brown
gold
green
pink
red
white

1. A skunk has a _____ stripe down the middle of his back.

2. _____ is for baby girls; blue is for baby boys.

3. Eddie didn't see that the light was _____, and the police pulled him over.

4. The spring rains help the grass to turn _____.

5. Some people think you will have bad luck if a _____ cat crosses your path.

6. After a leaf falls from a tree, it soon turns _____.

7. On a clear day, the sky is _____.

8. When you say that you will do something, is your word as good as _____ ?

3 **Read and Write.** Put the word that does not fit with the rest on the line to the right.

1. drive   hike   run   walk   _____

2. bedroom   dream   sleep   snore   _____

3. cap   hat   neck   scarf   _____

4. body   hip   leg   wrist   _____

5. bake   grill   raw   roast   _____

6. bear   fox   squirrel   whale   _____

7. beef   lamb   pork   shrimp   _____

8. Christmas   fall   spring   summer   _____

9. number   pair   twice   two   _____

10. hour   minute   week   yard   _____

11. jacket   shirt   slacks   vest   _____

12. ditch   dune   hole   pit   _____

4 **Read and Write.** Put *un-* in front of the words. Write the word that is made from the two parts on the line. Then put the new word in the right sentence.

un + safe = *unsafe*

un + less = _____

un + lucky = _____

un + happy = _____

un + wrapped = _____

1. Kate was _____ that she couldn't bake a cake that tasted any good.

2. Billy's aunt told him that he couldn't go to the movies _____ he cleaned his room first.

3. Many people think that thirteen is an _____ number.

4. When Mary felt *unsafe* in the house, she would go over to Aunt Louise's.

5. On Christmas morning, Billy _____ the gift from his cousin Mary first.

5 **Read and Write.** Put *re-* in front of the words. Write the word that is made from the two parts on the line. Then put the new word in the right sentence.

re + fuse = _refuse_

re + main = _____

re + mind = _____

re + paid = _____

re + turn = _____

1. Kate asked Linda to _____ the book by Friday.

2. Eddie _____ Bob as soon as he had the money.

3. Jack could never _refuse_ one of Aunt Louise's good dinners.

4. Mary's mother had to _____ Billy to make his bed each morning.

5. The teacher told Mary to _____ after class, so that she could help her with her math.

Lesson 20

Sounds for *c* and *g*

In these words, the **c** makes a **k** sound. This is called a **hard c**.

camp	coach	curb
carry	coast	curl
cast	comb	curve

In these words, the **c** makes an **s** sound. This is called a **soft c**.

cell	city	dance
cellar	cigar	chance
center	cigarette	ounce
ceiling		bounce

In these words, the **g** is like the **g** in **gas**. This is called a **hard g**.

guess	begin	bag
guest	began	flag
guilt	begun	dog
guilty		fog

In these words, the **g** makes a **j** sound. This is called a **soft g**.

germ	range
gin	strange
ginger	stranger
gingerbread	danger

Note the sound for **dge** in these words.

badge	bridge	dodge	fudge

Words for Study

answer	paycheck	shouldn't	hello
question	I'd	explain	anybody
wonder	groaned	happened	breakfast
tonight	silly	everything	snacks

Bob's Date with June

Aunt Louise stopped drying the dishes to answer the phone. When she knew it was Bob, she said, "Why, Bob, what's the matter? Your voice sounds strange."

"I feel like a dog asking you this question," said Bob, "but I wondered if you could lend me any money. I have a date tonight, and I didn't have a chance to pick up my paycheck."

"I'd love to help you out," answered Aunt Louise, "but, as a matter of fact, I'm broke, too."

"Well," groaned Bob, "I guess that's that. Nobody else I know seems to be home."

"Don't be so silly," said Aunt Louise. "You shouldn't feel guilty just because you don't have any money. Call June up and explain what happened. I'm sure everything will be all right."

Bob was beginning to feel a little better. "You know," he said, "that's just what I'm going to do." After he had hung up, he called June at once.

"Hello," said June.

"Hi, this is Bob," said Bob. "How are you?"

"Fine," answered June. "I was just mending the blouse I'm going to wear tonight. Your voice sounds strange. Is anything wrong?"

"I might as well tell you," said Bob. "I don't have any money to take you out to dinner tonight. I'm really sorry." Bob was beginning to lose his nerve. He just wanted to get off the phone as fast as he could. "Maybe we can go out next week," he said as he was about to hang up.

"Wait a minute," said June. "Money's no problem. I like my cooking better than anybody else's anyway. In fact, I just made my first gingerbread this afternoon. I'd love for you to be the first guest to try it."

Bob was so surprised that, at first, he couldn't speak. At last he said, "Do you really want me to come over?"

"Of course," answered June. "I'll fix us a nice meal, and we can talk or see what's on television tonight. Why don't you come over around seven o'clock?"

At seven o'clock on the dot, Bob knocked on June's front door. "Hi," said June. "I'm really glad to see you. Come on in."

When Bob got home that night, he thought he had just had the best time in his whole life. Just as Aunt Louise was always saying, "Good things can come out of bad things when people don't give up."

1 Read and Write.

ground *and* found

1. While walking in the woods, Dave _____ some money on the _____.

step *or* steep

2. "Watch your _____," said the bus driver to the people getting off the bus.

carry *or* marry

3. Bob hoped that, some day, he and June would _____.

city *and* pity

4. People who love the woods think it's a _____ that some people have to live in the _____.

steep *or* deep

5. The hill was so _____ that the Boy Scouts decided not to climb it.

Miss, Ms., *and* Mrs.

6. A woman who is not married is called _____ or _____. A woman who is married is called _____ or _____.

carve *and* starve

7. Mary thought that if her father didn't _____ the roast beef soon, she would _____.

but *and* butter

8. Andy wanted to make himself some toast, _____ he didn't have any _____ to put on it.

sweating *and* sweater

9. Mike was _____ so badly that he decided to take off his _____ .

sprawl *or* crawl

10. Most babies start to _____ way before their first birthday.

hard *and* hardly

11. Mary's math homework was so _____ that she _____ had any time to watch television.

wood, hood, *and* stood

12. The robber _____ in front of the pile of _____ with a _____ pulled over his head.

---

2 **Read and Write.** Choose the words that have to do with *breakfast* and put them in the first row. Put the words that have to do with *dinner* in the middle row. Put the words that have to do with *snacks* in the last row.
(USE EACH WORD ONLY ONCE.)

candy bar   popcorn
Coke   pork chops
corn flakes   pretzels
French toast   rice and beans
fried eggs   roast beef
ham and eggs   spare ribs
ice cream cone   stuffed peppers
pancakes

Breakfast	**Dinner**	**Snacks**
1. _____	1. _____	1. _____
2. _____	2. _____	2. _____
3. _____	3. _____	3. _____
4. _____	4. _____	4. _____
5. _____	5. _____	5. _____

3 **Twelve Questions.** Write *true* on the line if the sentence is true. Write *false* on the line if the sentence is false.

_____ 1. Cape Cod is on the East Coast.

_____ 2. Cats have fangs.

_____ 3. It is safe to skate on thin ice.

_____ 4. Deer can run faster than bears.

_____ 5. Food is cheaper to buy this year than it was last year.

_____ 6. Popcorn is made from flour.

_____ 7. The air in a city is cleaner than the air in the woods.

_____ 8. The catcher stands behind home plate.

_____ 9. The scores in football games are often higher than the scores in baseball games.

_____ 10. The time of day called *dusk* is in the morning.

_____ 11. When people blush, their faces turn blue.

_____ 12. I liked doing all the work in this reading book.

4 **Read and Write.** Answer these questions in good sentence form.

1. Do you put jam on your toast, or do you just use butter?

_____

2. When you don't know an answer, do you say that you don't know, or do you fake it?

_____

3. When you do your homework, do you like to write your answers, or do you like to print?

_____

4. Do you like pork chops better when they are fried or baked?

_____

5. When you get to the end of this reading book, do you plan to celebrate or take a long rest?

_____

First Review

Say these words out loud.

slam	slap	clap	class	clay	play
drain	drop	flop	flat	flare	glare
plan	plane	plug	shrug	shrunk	skunk
cash	crash	crop	shop	shake	flake
check	cheese	chew	flew	flock	block
east	each	beach	bleach	black	slacks
slice	slow	blow	blew	threw	three
drum	plum	plus	must	much	such

blame	chair	deep	best	bride	dip	brown	bunk
fame	fair	seep	chest	pride	hip	clown	funk
flame	hair	sleep	pest	side	slip	gown	skunk
shame	stair	steep	vest	wide	trip	town	trunk

1 **Read and Write.** Choose the best answer and write it on the line.

1. The ___*bull*___ got out of the pen and rushed toward the people who stood near the gate.
   (a) ball   (b) bell   (c) bill   (d) bull

2. Aunt Louise put the roses in a lovely pink _____.
   (a) base   (b) case   (c) chase   (d) vase

3. Do you rest in bed when you are _____, or do you keep on working?
   (a) sack   (b) sick   (c) soak   (d) sock

4. The man was so _____ that he had to bend over to get through the door.
   (a) take   (b) tale   (c) talk   (d) tall

5. Dick went to stay with his friends on the West _____ for Christmas.
   (a) Coach   (b) Coal   (c) Coast   (d) Coat

6. "Please _____ the door, so I can save a little on my heating bill," said Jack.
   (a) clock   (b) close   (c) cloth   (d) clothes

7. Bob was so much in love with June that he thought his _____ would burst.
   (a) hear   (b) heard   (c) heart   (d) heat

8. It seemed that no matter what Mary told Billy, her words went in one _____ and out the other.
   (a) each   (b) ear   (c) east   (d) eat

9. Dan looked all over for his computer, but he couldn't find it _____.
   (a) anybody   (b) anything   (c) anyway   (d) anywhere

10. How many times have you _____ in town this week?
    (a) beef   (b) been   (c) beep   (d) beer   (e) beet

11. Just as long as they did something that was fun, Eddie didn't _____ if they went to the amusement park or the movies.
    (a) car   (b) card   (c) care   (d) carry

12. When people sneeze, do you say "God _____ you"?
    (a) bleed   (b) bless   (c) blood   (d) blouse

2   **Read and Write.** Match the words that mean the same thing.

cash	_____	1. clean
crazy		
faint	_____	2. fast
gleam	_____	3. handy
mock		
patch	_____	4. make fun of
scrub	_____	5. money
strange		
swift	_____	6. nutty
useful		
	_____	7. odd
	_____	8. pass out
	_____	9. shine
	_____	10. mend

3 **Read and Write.** Match the words that are opposite in meaning.

answer
awake
calm
fire
huge
loaf
tame
thick
tired
waste

_____ 1. full of pep

_____ 2. hire

_____ 3. question

_____ 4. save

_____ 5. small

_____ 6. sleeping

_____ 7. thin

_____ 8. upset

_____ 9. wild

_____ 10. work

4 **Read and Write.** Use *a* or *an* in these sentences.

1. Aunt Louise fixed herself _____ egg and two slices of toast for breakfast.

2. Billy found _____ small pile of nuts that the squirrel had stored in the tree.

3. Driving forty miles _____ hour in a school zone is unsafe.

4. Have you ever watched _____ ant carry food?

5. Mack didn't have _____ answer to Joan's question.

6. Mary's mother asked Jack to keep _____ eye on Billy while she went shopping.

7. Sue rode _____ black horse on the path in the woods.

8. Roy hoped he would get _____ leading role in the school play.

9. The Boy Scout wore his badges to _____ meeting held at the school.

10. The king wore _____ gold crown when he gave a dinner party.

5 **Read and Write.** Choose the words that have to do with *land* and put them in the first row. Put the words that have to do with *sky* in the middle row. Put the words that have to do with *water* in the last row. (USE EACH WORD ONLY ONCE.)

	Land	**Sky**	**Water**
boats	1. _____	1. _____	1. _____
cities			
farms	2. _____	2. _____	2. _____
fish			
fog	3. _____	3. _____	3. _____
houses			
moon	4. _____	4. _____	4. _____
rain			
ships	5. _____	5. _____	5. _____
snow			
stars			
waves			
weeds			
whales			
woods			

Second Review

Say these words out loud.

brave	brain	drain	dream	cream	crime
crumb	thumb	thing	think	sink	sank
still	chill	child	mild	mind	blind
twist	wrist	wrong	strong	string	wing
march	match	patch	past	last	lost
climb	clip	trip	train	sprain	spray
skirt	shirt	short	shout	south	sound
shatter	platter	plate	place	plain	stain

age	class	dare	eel	file	cry	clip	blow
cage	gas	fare	feel	mile	dry	dip	flow
page	glass	flare	keel	pile	fly	hip	low
stage	grass	spare	peel	smile	fry	strip	slow
wage	pass	square	wheel	while	why	whip	show

1 **Read and Write.** Choose the best answer and write it on the line.

1. Roy was a brave, strong man, but when he saw a mouse, he felt _____.
   (a) harmless   (b) helpless   (c) hopeless   (d) jobless

2. Kate took such a huge _____ of popcorn that there was none left for Eddie.
   (a) handful   (b) harmful   (c) helpful   (d) useful

3. "We can't have pets where we're renting now," said the little boy _____.
   (a) firmly   (b) loudly   (c) lovely   (d) sadly   (e) safely

4. The fuse box was in the _____ near the two old tubs.
   (a) cellar   (b) center   (c) splinter   (d) stranger

5. "_____ the last time I try to bake a cake," said Kate firmly.
   (a) Don't   (b) Won't   (c) That's   (d) What's

6. "_____ only got twenty minutes to eat lunch today," said Dan.

 (a) I (b) I'll (c) I'm (d) I've

7. "_____ I see you downtown yesterday?" asked Linda.

 (a) Can't (b) Didn't (c) Couldn't (d) Shouldn't

8. "If you want to be a _____, you must know a lot about words," said Mary's father.

 (a) winner (b) wonder (c) worker (d) writer

9. When the boxer's eye started to bleed, they knew it would be _____ if he went on fighting.

 (a) unhappy (b) unlucky (c) unsafe (d) unwrap

10. Aunt Louise says that feeling _____ about hurting a friend's feelings is a waste of time. Just say you're sorry and get on with your life.

 (a) guilty (b) lucky (c) needy (d) rosy

2 **Numbers.** Use this list of words to answer the questions. (You will not need to use all the words on the list.)

one	six	eleven	sixteen	thirty
two	seven	twelve	seventeen	forty
three	eight	thirteen	eighteen	sixty
four	nine	fourteen	nineteen	ninety
five	ten	fifteen	twenty	million

_____ 1. How many months arc in a ycar?

_____ 2. How many days are in a week?

_____ 3. How many minutes are in an hour?

_____ 4. How many hours do you meet each week with your teacher?

_____ 5. What do most people think is an unlucky number?

_____ 6. What do most people think is a lucky number?

_____ 7. What is the sum of thirteen plus three?

_____ 8. How many lungs do you have?

_____ 9. How many spleens do you have?

_____ 10. How many cells are in your body?

3 **Read and Write.** Choose the right answers and write them on the lines.

1. Mother is to woman as _father_ is to man.
   (a) brother   (b) father   (c) female   (d) male

2. Shirt is to blouse as pants are to _____.
   (a) clothes   (b) legs   (c) men   (d) slacks

3. Beef is to cow as pork is to _____.
   (a) chops   (b) ham   (c) lamb   (d) pig

4. Loud is to soft as roar is to _____.
   (a) hushed   (b) kind   (c) lovely   (d) silly

5. Most is to least as best is to _____.
   (a) bad   (b) badly   (c) worse   (d) worst

6. Calm is to relaxed as mad is to _____.
   (a) cope   (b) mistake   (c) tired   (d) upset

7. Ground is to sky as floor is to _____.
   (a) ceiling   (b) house   (c) room   (d) top

8. Deer is to swift as _____ is to slow.
   (a) monkey   (b) skunk   (c) snail   (d) squirrel

4 **Word Pairs.** Use a word from the left row to put on the first line. Use a word from the right row to put on the last line.

black
bride
cats
ham
knife
reading
rod
✓ salt
Saturday
snakes
soap
thick

blue
dogs
eggs
fork
groom
✓ pepper
reel
snails
Sunday
thin
water
writing

1. Many people put this on their food.

   ___salt___ and _pepper_

2. You watch them get married.

   _____ and _____

3. This is the weekend.

   _____ and _____

4. You use these when you eat roast beef or steak.

   _____ and _____

5. Some people like this for breakfast.

   _____ and _____

6. You clean the dishes with

   _____ and _____

7. What are you learning more about in this class?

   _____ and _____

8. You need this for fishing.

   _____ and _____

9. If you're hurt badly, your skin turns

   _____ and _____

10. Some people fight like

    _____ and _____

11. According to an old verse, this is what little boys are made of.

    _____ and _____

12. Good friends see you through

    _____ and _____

5 **Read and Write.** Answer these questions in good sentence form.

1. Are you most happy in a big city, a small town, or the woods?

   _____

2. Do you use cream in your coffee, or do you think black coffee tastes better?

   _____

3. Do you think men are better drivers than women, or do you think women are better drivers?

   _____

4. When you feel you are in danger, do you freeze, or do you run for your life?

   _____

5. Which do you like best at an amusement park—the games, the rides, or the food?

   _____

6. Are you careful with money, or do you blow it as fast as you get it?

   _____

7. Do you think there should be a law that makes people use seat belts when they drive, or do you think people should make up their own minds about using them?

   _____

8. What do you think of the work you have done in this reading book?

   _____

9. Do you like telling other people how you feel about things, or do you like keeping your thoughts to yourself?

   _____

Word Index: Lessons 1-20

A
a
able
about
according
ace
across
act
add
after
afternoon
again
age
ago
aid
ail
air
all
all right
almost
alone
also
always
am
amuse
amusement
an
and
Andy
another
answer
ant
any
anybody
anything
anyway
anywhere
are
aren't
around
arm
armchair
art
as
ask
at
ate
aunt
awake
awoke

B
baby
back
bad
badge
badly
bag
bake
baker
bald
ball
band
bang
bank
banker
bar
bare
bark
barn
base
baseball
bat
batch
bath
bathroom
be
beach
bean
bear
beat
because
bed
bedroom
beef
been
beep
beer
beet
before
beg
began
begin
begun
behind
bell
belt
Ben
bend
bent
beside
best
bet
better
between

bib
big
bike
bill
Billy
bind
birth
birthday
bit
bite
black
blame
bleach
bleed
bless
blew
blind
block
blood
blouse
blow
blue
blush
board
boarder
boat
Bob
body
boil
bolt
bomb
bond
bone
bony
book
bore
born
boss
both
bounce
box
boxer
bow
boy
brain
brave
bread
breakfast
bride
bridge
broke
brother

brown
buck
Bucky
bud
bug
bulb
bull
bum
bump
bumper
bumpy
bun
bunk
bunt
burn
burner
burp
burst
bus
but
butter
buy
by

C
cab
cage
cake
call
calm
calmly
came
camp
can
candy
cane
can't
cap
cape
Cape Cod
car
card
care
careful
careless
carry
cart
carve
case
cash
cast
cat
catch

catcher
ceiling
celebrate
cell
cellar
cent
center
chair
chance
charm
chase
cheap
check
checkbook
cheese
chess
chest
chew
child
chill
chin
choose
chop
Christ
Christian
Christmas
chrome
church
cigar
cigarette
city
clap
class
clay
clean
cleaner
clear
climb
clip
clock
close
cloth
clothes
clown
club
coach
coal
coast
coat
cod
code
coffee

Coke
cold
comb
come
computer
cone
cook
cookbook
cool
cop
cope
copper
corn
cot
could
couldn't
count
course
court
cousin
cow
crash
crawl
crazy
cream
crib
crime
crop
cross
crowd
crown
crumb
cry
cub
cube
cup
cupcake
curb
curl
curve
cut
cute

D
dab
dad
daddy
dam
damp
Dan
dance
danger

dare
dark
dart
dash
date
Dave
day
dead
deal
dear
death
decide
deck
deep
deer
den
dent
desk
dice
Dick
did
didn't
die
dig
dime
dine
diner
dinner
dip
dirt
dish
ditch
dive
do
dock
dodge
does
dog
done
donkey
don't
door
doorway
dope
dot
down
downstairs
downtown
doze
Dr.
drain
dream

dress
drew
drive
driver
drop
drove
drum
dry
duck
due
dues
dug
duke
dull
dumb
dump
dune
dunk
during
dusk
Dutch

E
each
ear
east
eat
Eddie
eel
egg
eight
eighteen
eleven
else
end
ending
enough
even
evening
ever
everybody
everything
explain
eye

F
face
fact
fad
fade
fail
faint
fair
fake

fall
false
fame
fang
far
fare
farm
farmer
fast
fat
father
fed
fee
feed
feel
feet
fell
felt
female
fetch
few
fib
fifteen
fig
fight
fighter
file
fill
film
find
fine
fire
firm
firmly
first
fish
fist
fit
five
fix
flag
flake
flame
flare
flat
flew
flock
floor
flop
flour
flow
flush
fly
fog
fond

food
fool
foot
football
for
forget
fork
forty
found
four
fourteen
fox
free
freeze
French
fresh
Friday
friend
friendly
from
front
froze
fry
fudge
full
fume
fun
fund
funk
funny
fuse
fuss
fussy

G
game
gas
gate
gave
germ
get
gift
gin
ginger
gingerbread
girl
girlfriend
give
glad
gland
glare
glass
gleam
glue
go
goal

God
gold
gone
gong
good
goodness
got
gotten
gown
grade
grape
grass
gray
green
grill
groan
groom
ground
guess
guest
guilt
guilty
gum
gun
guy

H
had
hadn't
hair
hall
ham
hammer
hand
handful
handy
hang
happen
happy
hard
hardly
harm
harmful
harmless
hat
hate
have
haven't
hay
he
head
hear
heard
heart
heat

heck
heel
held
hello
help
helper
helpful
helpless
hen
her
herd
here
herself
hey
hi
hid
hide
hide-and-seek
high
high school
hike
hill
him
himself
hint
hip
hire
his
hit
hitter
hock
hold
hole
home
homeless
home run
homework
honk
hood
hop
hope
hopeless
horn
horse
hose
hot
hour
house
household
how
however
hug
huge
hum

hung
hunt
hunter
hurt
hush
hut

I
I
ice
ice cream
icy
I'd
idea
if
ill
I'll
I'm
in
ink
into
is
it
itch
it's
I've

J
jab
Jack
jack
jacket
jail
jam
jar
jaw
jazz
jeans
jeep
jerk
Joan
job
jobless
join
joint
joke
joker
Jones
jot
joy
jug
jump
June
junk
just

K
Kate
keel
keep
keeper
ketchup
key
kick
kid
kind
king
kiss
kit
kite
knee
knew
knife
knit
knock
know
known

L
lab
lace
lack
lacy
laid
lake
lamb
lame
lamp
land
lane
lap
lark
last
late
later
laugh
law
lay
lead
leaf
leak
lean
learn
least
led
left
leg
lend
lent
less
let

let's
lick
lid
lie
life
lifeboat
lift
light
like
lime
limp
Linda
line
lint
lip
list
lit
little
live
living
load
loaf
loan
lobby
lock
lone
long
look
lord
lose
loss
lost
lot(s)
loud
loudly
Louise
love
lovely
low
loyal
luck
lucky
lug
lump
lunch
lung

M
Mack
mad
made
maid
mail
main
make

male
man
manager
many
map
march
mark
marry
Mary
mask
mat
match
mate
math
matter
may
maybe
me
meal
mean
meat
meet
meeting
melt
men
mend
mess
messy
met
mice
middle
might
Mike
mile
mild
milk
million
mind
mine
mint
minute
miss
mistake
mitt
mix
mob
mock
mom
mommy
Monday
money
monkey
month
mood
moon

mop
more
morning
most
mother
mouse
movie
Mr.
Mrs.
Ms.
much
mud
muddy
mug
mugger
mule
muse
must
mute
my
myself

N

nail
name
nap
near
neat
neck
need
needy
nerve
net
never
new
next
nice
nick
night
nine
nineteen
ninety
no
nobody
nod
none
noon
nope
north
nose
nosy
not
note
notebook
nothing
now

nude
numb
number
nurse
nut
nutty

O

oar
o'clock
odd
of
off
often
oil
okay
old
on
once
one
only
open
opposite
or
other
ounce
our
out
outside
oven
over

P

pace
pack
pad
page
paid
pain
paint
painter
painting
pair
pale
pan
pancake
pant
pants
park
part
party
pass
past
pat
patch
path

paw
pay
paycheck
payday
payment
pea
pear
peck
peek
peel
peer
pen
penny
people
pep
pepper
pest
pet
phone
pick
picture
pie
pig
pile
pin
pine
Ping-Pong
pink
pit
pity
place
plain
plan
plane
plate
platter
play
player
please
plug
plum
plus
pod
point
poke
pole
police
pond
pool
poor
pop
popcorn
Pope
pork
pot

pour
pray
pretzel
price
pride
print
prize
problem
proud
prune
pull
pulse
pump
punt
purse
put

Q

quack
queer
question
quick
quickly
quit
quite
quote

R

race
rack
rage
raid
rain
rake
ram
ramp
ran
rang
range
rank
rare
rat
rate
raw
reach
read
ready
real
really
red
reel
refund
refuse
relax
remain
remind

rent
repaid
rest
return
rib
rice
rich
rid
ride
rig
right
ring
rip
ripe
risk
road
roar
roast
rob
robber
robbery
robe
rock
rod
rode
role
roll
room
rope
rose
rosy
rot
row
Roy
royal
rub
rude
rug
rule
ruler
run
rung
runt
rush

S

sack
sad
sadly
safe
safely
sale
salt
same

sand
sang
sank
sat
Saturday
save
saw
say
saying
says
scar
scare
scarf
school
score
scout
scratch
scream
screech
screen
scrub
seat
see
seed
seek
seem
seen
seep
self
sell
send
sent
serve
set
seven
seventeen
shake
shame
share
sharp
shatter
she
shift
shine
ship
shirt
shock
shop
short
shortstop
should
shouldn't
shout
show
shrank

shrimp
shrink
shrug
shrunk
sick
side
sight
silly
since
sing
singer
sink
sip
sit
six
sixteen
sixty
skate
skill
skin
skirt
skunk
sky
slacks
slam
slap
sleep
sleeve
slice
slip
slow
slush
small
smart
smash
smell
smile
smoke
snack
snail
snake
sneeze
snore
snow
so
soak
soap
sob
sock
soft
sole
some
something
song
soon

sore
sorry
sort
sound
sour
south
space
spank
spare
speak
spill
spit
spite
splash
spleen
splint
splinter
split
spoon
spot
sprain
sprawl
spray
spring
sprint
square
squeak
squeal
squeeze
squirrel
stage
stain
stair
stale
stand
star
start
starve
stay
steak
steam
steep
step
steer
still
stood
stop
store
stork
story
strange
stranger
straw
stream
street